TIME
LIFE
BOOKS
®

LIFE WORLD LIBRARY

LIFE NATURE LIBRARY

TIME READING PROGRAM

THE LIFE HISTORY OF THE UNITED STATES

LIFE SCIENCE LIBRARY

GREAT AGES OF MAN

TIME-LIFE LIBRARY OF ART

TIME-LIFE LIBRARY OF AMERICA

FOODS OF THE WORLD

THIS FABULOUS CENTURY

LIFE LIBRARY OF PHOTOGRAPHY

LIFE NATURE LIBRARY

THE REPTILES

by Archie Carr
and the Editors of
TIME-LIFE BOOKS

TIME-LIFE BOOKS   NEW YORK

About the Author

Archie Carr, though born in Mobile, Alabama, has long been as much a part of Florida as the reptiles there he knows and loves so well. He went to college at the University of Florida, received his M.S. and his Ph.D. there and has taught in the biology department of that institution since 1937. Today he is a graduate research professor at the university, but is known far beyond the boundaries of Florida as probably the greatest authority on sea turtles in the world. Fascinated by turtles and snakes from the time he was a boy, Dr. Carr's studies have taken him to distant places as a biologist and adviser to corporations, commissions and governments. He is particularly identified with the Caribbean Conservation Corporation, an organization dedicated to saving the green turtle from extinction, but he has also worked extensively on other continents, notably Africa. A prolific writer as well as scientist, he is the author of six books, numerous scientific papers and several short stories, one of which won the O. Henry Award in 1956. That same year he also won the Daniel Giraud Elliott medal for pre-eminence in zoology and the John Burroughs medal for nature writing.

ON THE COVER: In a head-on view, a bamboo viper from Formosa gleams like polished jade. The deep pits between the red eyes are heat-sensing organs that help this poisonous snake to locate and strike its warm-blooded prey.

Published simultaneously in Canada. Reprinted 1971.
Library of Congress catalogue card number 63-12781.
School and library distribution by Silver Burdett Company, Morristown, New Jersey.

Contents

TIME-LIFE BOOKS

EDITOR
Jerry Korn
EXECUTIVE EDITOR
A. B. C. Whipple
PLANNING
Oliver E. Allen
TEXT DIRECTOR   ART DIRECTOR
Martin Mann   Sheldon Cotler
CHIEF OF RESEARCH
Beatrice T. Dobie
PICTURE EDITOR
Robert G. Mason
Assistant Text Directors:
Ogden Tanner, Diana Hirsh
Assistant Art Director: Arnold C. Holeywell
Assistant Chief of Research: Martha T. Goolrick
Assistant Picture Editor: Melvin L. Scott

PUBLISHER
Joan D. Manley
General Manager: John D. McSweeney
Business Manager: John Steven Maxwell
Sales Director: Carl G. Jaeger
Promotion Director: Beatrice K. Tolleris
Public Relations Director: Nicholas Benton

LIFE NATURE LIBRARY

EDITOR: Maitland A. Edey
Assistant to the Editor: John Purcell
Copy Editor: Percy Knauth
Designer: Paul Jensen
Staff Writers: David Bergamini, Dale Brown,
Robert McClung, Peter Meyerson
Chief Researcher: Martha Turner
Researchers: Gerald A. Bair, David Beckwith,
Doris Bry, Robert Cowen, Susan Freudenheim,
Le Clair G. Lambert, Paula Norworth,
Susan Rayfield, Phyllis M. Williamson

EDITORAL PRODUCTION
Production Editor: Douglas B. Graham
Quality Director: Robert L. Young
Assistant: James J. Cox
Copy Staff: Rosalind Stubenberg, Suzanne Seixas, Florence Keith
Picture Department: Dolores A. Littles, Joan T. Lynch
Art Assistants: James K. Davis, Mark A. Binn

The text for this book was written by Archie Carr, the picture essays by the staff. The following individuals and departments of Time Inc. were helpful in producing the book: LIFE staff photographers Larry Burrows, Alfred Eisenstaedt, Eliot Eliosofon, Fritz Goro and Nina Leen; Editorial Production, Robert W. Boyd Jr., Margaret T. Fischer; Editorial Reference, Peter Draz; Picture Collection, Doris O'Neil; Photographic Laboratory, George Karas; TIME-LIFE News Service, Murray J. Gart; Reprints staff: Paula Arno (editor).

Introduction

REPTILES have been around for some 300 million years, but they came into their own just a few decades ago—at least in the mind of the average American. Part of this latter-day awakening of interest and tolerance may stem from the flood of recent herpetological research, but much more originates from public awareness, at long last, that most reptiles, serpents included, are of interest and value, and not all are horrendous monsters fit only to be slaughtered at every opportunity.

Probably the long-extinct dinosaurs have contributed their share to this improved state of affairs. At least they are familiar to all of us, thanks to the restorations of the paleontologists. We see their likenesses frequently—in cartoons and advertisements, as small boys' toys, or in the "bones" at the museum—and usually they are portrayed as symbols of power and life in the raw during bygone millennia. But the baby turtle, the "chameleon" bought at the circus and the pet garter snake, which find their way into so many private homes, are the stuff from which enthusiasm springs among the youth of today. They ensure a large and appreciative audience for this book about a remarkable group of animals by a gifted and eloquent professor of biology.

If only we could see for ourselves some of the grotesque monsters of yesteryear! In a sense we have come too late. We are witnessing the closing scene of the last act of a natural drama that has known no equal. Arising from feeble ancestors in a new and hostile environment, the reptiles branched out in all directions and for a long time were dominant. Those that survive are meager remnants of the long-dead hordes, and at least some—the turtles, crocodiles and tuatara—eminently qualify for that hackneyed but beautifully descriptive appellation of living fossils.

There may be a lesson for us in the rise and fall of the great reptiles. We human beings are riding high today, and many of us give little thought to the future despite the threat of atomic war, our fantastically burgeoning population and our profligate wastage of natural resources. Let one or more of these dangers pass beyond control, and mankind may find itself vastly reduced in numbers and struggling for survival as so many of the reptiles are today. There is much food for thought in Dr. Carr's concluding chapter.

At least some of the reptiles are making a comeback, or they were until we began polluting our streams, poisoning our countryside with insect sprays and bulldozing so many of their habitats out of existence. These are the snakes and the lizards, creatures that, in their own ways, are fully as fascinating as *Tyrannosaurus*, *Brontosaurus* and *Pteranodon* of the Age of Reptiles. So in fact are all the rest of the surviving groups, particularly the turtles, which are Dr. Carr's first love and passionate interest. This is a wonderful book. You will enjoy reading it and will learn a lot as you do.

ROGER CONANT
Director and Curator of Reptiles, Philadelphia Zoological Garden
Research Associate, The American Museum of Natural History
and The Academy of Natural Sciences of Philadelphia

1

The "Cold-Blooded" Fraternity

THE reactions of the little girl on the opposite page epitomize the feelings of people generally about reptiles. Most people have a vague feeling that no reptiles except turtles are to be trusted, and so make no effort to find out anything about them or even to learn what they are. It would scarcely be necessary in writing a book about birds, say, to make sure at the outset that the reader knew what birds were, but in the case of reptiles this is sadly true. Therefore one should start with a definition that excludes frogs, toads, platypuses, mudskippers, armadillos and a good many other odd animals which are constantly being mistakenly lumped with reptiles.

A proper reptile, to begin with, is a vertebrate animal. It has scales, breathes air (not water), characteristically lays shelled eggs and depends on outside sources for its body heat. There are in the world only five main groups of animals that fit this definition. They are the turtles, the lizards, the snakes, the crocodilians, and a strange, little-seen creature called the tuatara, which looks like a lizard but is not. In these latest days of geologic history, there are about 6,000 species of reptiles scattered over the earth. Though they are most diverse and numerous in warm regions, they range far northward too, turning up in

THE ABUNDANCE OF REPLITLES TODAY

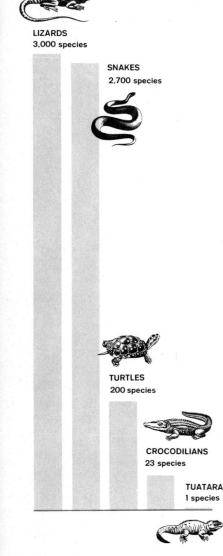

LIZARDS
3,000 species

SNAKES
2,700 species

TURTLES
200 species

CROCODILIANS
23 species

TUATARA
1 species

Of the 16 orders of reptiles known from fossils, only four have managed to survive until modern times. The largest by far, the Squamata, combines both lizards and snakes, with a grand total of about 5,700 living species. By contrast, there are only 200 species of turtles and 23 species of crocodilians throughout the world, and the tuatara alone in New Zealand. The last two were not always so scarce. Fossils of at least 108 species of extinct crocodilians are known. And the rhynchocephalian order, to which the tuatara belongs, has numbered at least 23 species.

the yards of rural Swedes, Siberians and citizens of the state of Maine. They even occur on the dusty deserts of the world.

It so happens that I live in Florida, which is one of the good reptile regions. I have a farm with woods around it and a marshy pond out in front. The place offers a fine sampling of the main groups of reptiles. The farm is no Cretaceous swamp, but through the years we have caught, seen, stepped on or had the house invaded by a great many different kinds of reptiles, representing all the main groups except the tuatara.

To begin with, the farm is extraordinarily blessed with turtles, and a stroll around it gives a good, broad impression of turtle architecture and customs. The turtles there are both aquatic and terrestrial. They spread in size from the four-inch stinkjims to snappers that weigh 30 pounds or more and in disposition from the long-necked, short-tempered, carnivorous soft-shells that lurk on the pond bottom snorkeling air through tubular nostrils to the various placid, dome-shelled water turtles, called cooters in Florida, which bask on logs, forage for edible trash on the bottom or cruise about chomping at fallen cow-crazy petals floating on the water. Industrious gopher turtles follow their small trails out from vaulted burrows and graze among the grazing cows. Once in a long while a box turtle comes meditating through the yard and retires to its shell until we go away. Turtles are the most conservative of living reptiles, and the box turtle seems to me the spiritual essence of turtle mildness and conservatism.

In calling turtles conservative I have mainly in mind their sticking to an ancestral architecture devised a very long time ago—certainly not the architecture itself, which is about the most bizarre modification of vertebrate structure ever made. For the specialty of turtles is armor, a shell made up of a top part (the carapace) and a belly part (the plastron). The two parts are generally joined at each side by a bony bridge. Top and bottom, the shell has two layers, an outer one made up of broad, horny scales joined by stout seams and an inner, usually much thicker layer of tightly jointed bones. Because the seams of these two mosaics do not coincide, the whole structure forms an extremely strong casing within which much, and in some cases all, of the turtle can be safely stowed away.

THE origin of this shell has not been convincingly revealed by paleontologists, and so it is not possible to say just where in the reptile record the turtle line begins. A little reptile called Eunotosaurus that lived some 250 million years ago in the Permian age is often pointed to as a probable turtle ancestor. It had ribs which were broadened in a way that suggests a rudimentary shell. But whatever the beginnings of turtles may have been, the shell is now the mark of the creature. In spite of the millions of years of evolution that have seen turtles established nearly everywhere on the earth except in the air, the shell, in some readily recognizable form, has been retained.

The advantage the shell brought must have been strong, because it is not an easy thing to live with. Embryologically, it is a sort of nightmare. To live in it and keep their front legs working right, turtles had to rearrange their shoulder girdle, bringing it back into an unprecedented position inside the rib case. This is not a thing that happened once back in the Permian and then was done forever. Each time an embryo becomes a turtle it happens all over again, just as each baby flounder is first an upright fish with an eye properly on either side, and then later becomes flattened, with both eyes on the same side.

The shell has also dictated a change in the method of breathing. Because a turtle cannot expand its chest at all, it must suck in air by moving things about inside. By contracting a pair of muscles back at the flanks, the turtle can increase the volume of the space around the lungs, and the air rushes in. To expel air, it contracts another set of muscles under the viscera, pushing the internal organs forward to squeeze against the lungs. A number of other physiological adjustments makes breathing a distinctive process in turtles and, incidentally, one about which a great deal remains to be learned.

Turtles range in weight from a few ounces to well over half a ton. The biggest turtles are aquatic, but there are big ones on land too. The famous Galápagos tortoises, and others on islands in the Indian Ocean, have reached weights of over 400 pounds. During the Pleistocene, there were even bigger ones in various parts of the world.

T HERE is a popular notion that turtles live, as it were, forever. Little is known scientifically about their maximum life span, however, and it is not possible to evaluate this notion. Careful sifting of records from zoos, and of the generally shaky evidence afforded by turtles with dates carved into their shells, has led some herpetologists, as students of reptiles are called, to suggest a figure of a hundred years as a probable maximum. Few turtles living near man realize this potentiality. They get run over on the road, their marshes or ponds are drained, their streams are poisoned, or they are simply caught and eaten. Fortunately for their survival, their longevity does not mean they are slow to mature. In fact, turtles reach sexual maturity in a surprisingly short time. In the several species for which data are available, including some of the big sea turtles, breeding may begin at ages of from three to eight years.

The most distinctive of living turtles is the giant leatherback sea turtle. Though it looks like a turtle, it has no proper turtle shell, but only a rubbery skin covering a mosaic of little, pebblelike bones which have nothing to do with the broad bones of the ordinary turtle carapace and are not connected to the skeleton at all. While the four other genera of sea turtles show some modification of the bony carapace, their shells are more like those of land and freshwater turtles. Another turtle group that stands apart is that of the soft-shelled, or pancake, turtles, distributed in Africa, Asia and North America. In these the horny shell is also replaced by a continuous skin, and the edge is thin, floppy cartilage with no supporting marginal bones.

The motley array of the remaining kinds of turtles falls into two main groups, according to the way they draw in their necks. Most of them, the Cryptodira (hidden necks), retire with the neck bent into a vertically folding, S-shaped curve. They are found in Europe, Asia, Africa and the Americas. The other group, the side-necked turtles (Pleurodira), brings the neck in sideways and lays it along the body under the fore eaves of the shell. Side-necks are confined to tropics of the southern continents, Africa, South America and Australia. One of them is the famous matamata (*Chelys fimbriata*), the most grotesque-looking of all the turtles. The matamata, in fact, does not look like a turtle at all; it looks like a pile of leaves. In Colombia, where it is fairly common in swampy streams, and where a particular region contains a strain of extremely homely Indians, the women of this group are sometimes referred to as having *cara de matamata*, the face of a matamata. I judge that this is not said to their faces.

From the standpoint of abundance and diversity, the lizards and snakes are by far the most flourishing reptiles of today. Between them the two groups include about 600 genera and at least 5,700 species. They occur on every conti-

STRUCTURAL TROUBLES OF TURTLES

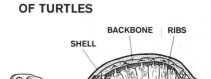

The internal rearrangements that a turtle has to put up with in order to live inside a hard shell are drastic. The creature's backbone has become fused to the shell. Its ribs are flattened and widened like fence palings to ensure maximum support. Its shoulder blades and hips are inside what would be the chest of a more conventional vertebrate. Its neck is long and flexible and can be retracted in an S-curve, pulling the head inside the shell for safety.

HOW LIZARDS DIFFER FROM SNAKES

Although lizards and snakes belong to the same reptilian order, they have clearly visible differences. A typical lizard moves about on four limbs. It hears air-borne sounds through external ear openings, and sees with an eye which may be covered by two movable eyelids. The typical snake, on the other hand, moves by undulating its body and is aided by broad ventral scales which catch against the ground and keep it from slithering backward. It can only hear through its skull bones, which transmit vibrations from the ground. A glassy transparent scale covers its unwinking eye.

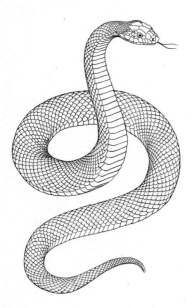

nent except Antarctica. Snakes are clearly derived from some ancient kind of lizard, and the two are put together in the order Squamata.

One of the features distinguishing the lizards and snakes from other reptiles is a drastic reduction of bones in the temporal region of the skull, which reaches its extreme among the snakes. Another is that the anal opening in lizards and snakes is transverse, instead of longitudinal as in crocodilians and turtles. Finally, both snakes and lizards have paired copulatory organs, and both have distinctive sets of sensory cells in their mouths, called Jacobson's organs.

As to differences between snakes and lizards themselves, most lizards can close their eyes, but a snake's eyes remain permanently open behind a clear covering called the spectacle. The unblinking stare of snakes may account for some of the superstitious fears people have about them. Snakes also generally have a single row of widened scales under the belly, while the scales of lizards tend to be more nearly the same size above and below. Lizards typically have some sort of external ear; snakes have none. In most lizards the tail can be readily shed, evidently as an escape mechanism. In some, the broken-off section snaps and jumps about in an irresponsible way. It is easy to imagine that this allows the rest of the lizard to slip quietly away from the scene while its attacker is preoccupied with the twitching tail. Later, a new tail generally grows again, sometimes lighter in color, with a different scale pattern and shorter than the one that was left behind.

The most obvious difference between typical lizards and snakes, however, is the leglessness of the latter. Although there are lizards that have no legs and that superficially resemble snakes, it is still generally easy to draw the line between the two groups. At the same time, it also is helpful to keep in mind that snakes are really a specialized and quite successful sort of lizard.

OF the two groups of the Squamata, the lizards are of course the older. They have the conventional body plan of a typical land vertebrate: four legs, five toes to a foot, and the sprawling gait of the earliest reptiles. Most of the adaptations that have allowed them to spread and prosper are relatively unspectacular changes in the old four-legged look—exceptions being the various groups in which the legs have been lost completely. As vertebrates, lizards are a fairly representative group and it has been suggested that the lizard would be more suitable as a type with which to introduce freshman biology students to vertebrate anatomy than the universally used frog. Perhaps it sounds cynical to say so, but I think the answer there is that the frog, being tailless, fits dissection pans more gracefully.

In spite of their fundamentally conventional body plan, modern lizards are a diverse lot. They range in length from two inches to 10 feet. They may look like dragons and they may look like worms, and they show a complex adaptive range through terrestrial, arboreal, subterraneous and aquatic environments.

Out at my farm lizards are all over the place on warm days. The large family of the Iguanidae is there, represented by the slender anole that stalks insects on the screens, and by the scaly-backed fence lizards that bask on almost every log or stump. This is, as the name suggests, the group to which the big tropical arboreal and marine iguanas belong, and it includes a host of smaller forms. Its counterpart in the Old World is the family Agamidae, which has a curiously similar structural and ecological spread.

The classic lizards—classic because they are of the Old World and since early times have beguiled European naturalists—are the personable lacertas of the family Lacertidae. My farm is, of course, devoid of lacertas, and this is a shame. Their place is partly taken by the athletic, silky skinned, six-lined race-runner, *Cnemidophorus*, a member of the related family Teiidae. The teiids are an alert and active lot of lizards that mostly occur in South America but are also found foraging about dooryards among chickens and babies in villages throughout the Caribbean. At the farm the racerunner streaks across the paths, and throughout the summer the hot, bare sand in all the open places is slashed with its tracks.

The most cosmopolitan lizard family is that of the skinks, the Scincidae—shiny-scaled lizards with protrusible tongues and a generally surreptitious air, which may account for their being occasionally known as scorpions. One of the farm skinks, the ground lizard, is a brown slip not much bigger than an old wooden match. The other is the big, burnished redheaded scorpion, which irks squirrel hunters with the noise it makes skittering up the trunks of trees.

A DAY of plowing or harrowing is likely to turn up two kinds of lizards that have no legs. One is the so-called glass snake, which dashes headlong into the soil and makes one wonder why a European relative is known as the slowworm. The other is the Florida worm lizard, a blind, pink, double-ended creature like a blunt night-crawler worm. The worm-lizard family is called Amphisbaenidae, literally meaning "to walk on both ends," because among most of the creatures in it both ends look surprisingly alike. As these two burrowers show, snakes were not the only legless descendants of the ancestral lizard stocks. Through the world list of lizard families, legless members repeatedly turn up, a drastic adaptation that seems odd to a beast as dependent on his legs as man.

The giants among modern lizards are the monitors (family Varanidae), which are believed to be close to the ancestral line from which snakes came. In the East Indies, there is a monitor aptly if over-sensationally known as the Komodo "dragon" that reaches a length of over 10 feet, and there are African and Asian species that by far exceed the average size for modern lizards. Monitors are fierce predators which run down and rend quite large prey. They have long, flexible necks, protrusible tongues like snakes, and an intense way of looking at people that makes them feel uneasy.

There are no monitors on the farm, nor indeed are there any wild ones anywhere in the Western Hemisphere. There are no real chameleons out there either, or any Gila monsters. But the greatest deprivation we suffer is the lack of geckos. To residents of the tropics all over the world, the geckos—lizards of the family Gekkonidae—are a familiar institution. Geckos have many features that endear them to the open-minded. They live trustingly in people's houses. They have loose skins, vertical pupils, no eyelids and a voice—the only voice among lizards and one of the few really reliable voices in the whole class of reptiles. The name gecko is an effort at onomatopoeia, being suggestive of the sounds made by an Old World species known technically (and a bit redundantly) as *Gekko gekko*. A South African gecko, *Ptneopus garrulus*, gets its specific name from the habit of calling vociferously from the mouths of burrows that it makes on hillsides. Almost everybody who knows geckos is fond of them. Even people who mistakenly believe they are poisonous seem secretly pleased to have them around. The herpetologist Clifford Pope speaks of their magnetism and suggests that they may surpass baby turtles as potential pets. I agree, with but one reservation: a child is apt to be horrified when a gecko reacts to having its tail pulled by simply dropping off the tail into the child's hand.

A DISPOSABLE TAIL

At the touch of a badger, a fence lizard gives its hungry foe the slip by dropping its tail. This disconcerting defense is used by many lizards. The spot where the tail can break off is preset by a crack in a vertebra, and the muscles nearby are also arranged so they will separate neatly. As if this sudden splitting of one succulent morsel into two were not enough, the predator's momentary confusion is increased by the lively twisting and turning of the severed tail, while the little lizard darts off in safety to grow a new one.

We come now to the snakes, and it is interesting, in the light of their close relationship to, and derivation from, lizards, that some of the most primitive living snakes are burrowers whose skeletons retain traces of the old limb girdles from ancient lizard times. One family, the worm snakes (family Typhlopidae), is made up of tiny species with much reduced eyes and teeth, blunt heads, little scales and even the remnants of a pelvis. They have some features that have led some experts to suggest that they are not snakes at all, but are actually aberrant lizards.

Much better known, more conspicuous and far more numerous are the four principal snake families, the Boidae, the Colubridae, the Viperidae and the Elapidae. The first of these, and the most primitive, includes the New World boas and anacondas, and the pythons of the Old World tropics. They are constrictors: they kill their prey by wrapping themselves around it and squeezing. Although there are some small members of the group, the Boidae as a family are notorious for being the largest snakes in the world. There are well-authenticated records of anacondas more than 37 feet long, pythons of 33 feet, boa constrictors of 18 feet. Generally speaking, pythons and boas resemble each other closely, but the former lay eggs and the latter bear live young. There are also slight skeletal differences between them.

THE second major snake family, the Colubridae, is by far the most diversified. It contains about two thirds of the world's snakes which, for want of a better name, go under the general heading of "typical" snakes. There are colubrids wherever snakes are found. As might be expected, they are the most numerous and most varied snakes on my Florida farm. Within a hundred yards of the house you can find snakes to show the main colubrid habits and habitats. Down at the pond edge, for instance, if you go to see why a frog is screaming, you will probably find that a water snake—a banded or green water snake—has hold of it, or perhaps a common garter snake. Or if it is a tiny, thin scream it may be that a ribbon snake is trying to swallow a gangling tree frog. The most ubiquitous snakes on the place are the black snake and the rat snake, or chicken snake. The two belong to different but related groups with worldwide distribution. The chicken snake is an *Elaphe*, a slow-moving, mainly arboreal constrictor, most readily found by joining any conclave of irate blue jays. The black snake belongs to the genus *Coluber*, which, with the whip snakes, includes some of the most agile and enterprising snakes in the world.

The farm colubrids range in size from a scarce red-bellied *Storeria* that creeps about in leaf mold and matures at a length of five inches to the handsome gun-metal indigo snake that can swallow a rabbit. The rear-fang contingent—the typical snakes that have independently hit upon poison as a device to get food—is represented by the crown snake, *Tantilla*, which has grooved fangs but is too small to get a grip on a human. You can dig up a scarlet snake a foot underground, or chase a coachwhip over many acres, or see a slender twig on a bush turn into the air-thin grace of *Opheodrys*, the rough green snake. Most of the typical snakes on the place lay eggs, but some bear their young alive. Some eat any living prey they can catch and swallow, but the hog-nosed snakes lean heavily on toads for food, the king snake eats other snakes, and the red-bellied, shiny horn snake in the pond eats mostly salamanders.

The remaining snakes of the farm and of the world constitute two groups among which the production and injection of venom have become highly refined adaptations. These are the vipers and the cobras, the latter group including the coral snakes and sea snakes. The cobras and their relatives (family Elapidae) are found around the world in tropical regions. They kill prey by venom injected through fixed hollow or grooved fangs located toward the front of the upper jaw. They are generally slender as compared with vipers, and except for one Australian species their heads are not markedly broadened or heart-shaped. Some of them, like the mambas of Africa, are big, swift, obstreperous and even warlike. Others are timid burrowers or foragers in leaf mold, like most of the American coral snakes. The king cobra of India with its frightening hood reaches a top length of about 18 feet, but some of the burrowing elapids may be only a few inches long, with a gape of mouth too narrow for biting people. In Australia, the cobralike snakes by far outnumber the typical snakes. There is a fantastic variety of species there, including such creatures as the dreaded tiger snake, the death adder and the 12-foot taipan, perhaps the most ferocious snake in the world when provoked.

THE poisonous snakes with the most elaborate venom-injection apparatus are the vipers (family Viperidae). They are found on all the continents except Australia; in fact, most poisonous snakes of temperate regions are vipers. There are two well-marked groups of them: the true vipers (subfamily Viperinae), confined to the Old World; and the pit vipers (subfamily Crotalinae), which have both American and Asiatic members but are mainly concentrated in the New World. Most vipers are stout-bodied snakes with the wedge-shaped or heart-shaped head generally thought of as the mark of a poisonous snake. The pit vipers include such imposing animals as the rattlesnakes and the tropical American fer-de-lance and bushmaster. Their name is derived from a sensory depression, or pit, in the side of the snout between the eye and the nostril. This is elaborately supplied with nerves and blood vessels and is an organ specialized for detecting the presence and range of warm objects. Most pit vipers eat warm-blooded prey, and the pit is no doubt used primarily in feeding, but like the rattle of the rattlesnake it is perhaps also of value as a means of avoiding injury under the hoofs of big mammals.

A GIANT SCAVENGER

The Komodo "dragon," named for the East Indian island where it was first found, is the largest living lizard. A voracious and undiscriminating carnivore, it will eat any kind of carrion, as well as living animals. Lethargic when it has fed, this monitor lizard shows surprising spurts of speed when hungry, and uses its long, strong tail with lethal dexterity.

The only way my farm stands out in the serpent-rich north Florida landscape is in the prevalence of poisonous snakes there. A coral snake on the lawn is no great event at all. Cottonmouth moccasins come up from the pond—every now and then the cook kills one at the kitchen door. Diamondback rattlesnakes are abundant, and pygmy rattlers turn up occasionally underfoot. In fact, a snake found in the yard is almost if not quite as likely to be venomous as harmless, and this is by no means the case in most places.

We have had five children ranging the premises for a dozen years and they have to date remained unbitten. The only friction we have had with snakes has been their killing of our dogs. A series of low-slung dogs has lived on the place—trustful bassets, and testy dachshunds opposed to all forms of life not canine or human. Of these, three, and perhaps four, have been killed by snakes.

LIKE any proper Florida pond, ours has an alligator in it. Alligators belong to the order Crocodilia, the third major group of reptiles, which includes three living families. One of these, the Alligatoridae, has in it the familiar American alligator, its close relative the Chinese alligator and the various tropical American caimans. The second family is the Crocodylidae, the true crocodiles, dwarf crocodiles and the false gavial. The third, the Gavialidae, has a single living representative, the slim-jawed, fish-eating gavial of southern Asia.

Crocodilia are in some respects the most advanced of reptiles. They share with higher vertebrates a four-chambered heart. This makes possible a more efficient circulation than other reptiles have, because in the usual reptilian three-chambered heart there is some mixing of newly oxygenated blood from the lungs with the deoxygenated blood just in from the tissues of the body. Another advanced feature of crocodilians is a partition between the cavities of the chest and abdomen that suggests the diaphragm of mammals. In crocodilians the cloacal opening is a longitudinal slit as in turtles, instead of being transverse as in lizards and snakes.

Full-grown crocodilians range in size from between three and four feet, in the case of the Congo dwarf crocodile and the dwarf caiman, to top lengths of about 23 feet in the Orinoco crocodiles. The biggest American alligator ever measured was slightly over 19 feet long. How long crocodilians live is not certain, although they have long been thought of as practically indestructible creatures that live forever. In the rare places in which they are not killed long before that by man they probably do reach ages of 50 years or more. They appear to mature at an age of six or seven years.

Crocodilians have one of the few well-developed voices among reptiles. In its timbre and impact on the surroundings, the voice of the American alligator must be considered one of the great animal voices of the world. It is a matter of family pride that the alligator which nearly a decade ago appeared at a tender age in our pond finally began to sing. For six years he had cruised silently about, methodically eating or driving off other alligators that came in from other places, and cracking mud turtles with a ghastly noise that disgusted my daughter. Then one misty morning he came forth with the earth-shaking, soul-stirring song of his kind. I suppose this means he is growing up. Or she—the females bellow too.

The remaining order of living reptiles, the Rhynchocephalia, has one living representative. This is the tuatara, *Sphenodon punctatus*. There are no tuataras on our farm. They live only on a few islands off the coast of New Zealand, and their story will be told in a later chapter.

THE TOKAY GECKO, A FOOT-LONG LIZARD OF ASIA, IS ONE OF THE FEW REPTILES TO LIVE WITH MAN—IT IS AN EXPERT INSECT CATCHER

The Venerable Reptiles

Once the dominant form of life on earth, the reptiles are now vastly reduced in numbers and variety. They persist today in three main groups—the turtles, the lizards and snakes, and the crocodilians—plus one almost extinct form, the little-known tuatara. Many are relatively unchanged from the age when dinosaurs rumbled over the land, and offer fascinating hints as to what life was like then.

The Anatomy of a Reptile

Although no single reptile can be considered typical of all reptiles, the alligator is as good a representative as any, since it has a backbone, is cold-blooded, lays eggs with shells and has a reptilian skin—i.e., either slated, scaled or shell-like. Nevertheless it has advanced features which are peculiar to it. Its four-chambered heart is more efficient than the three-chambered hearts of other reptiles, which tend to mix freshly oxygenated blood with unoxygenated

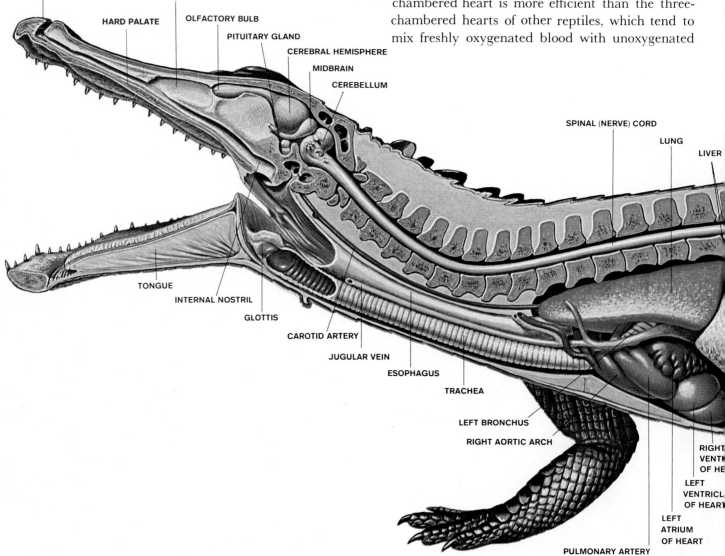

MOUTH. To achieve its characteristic gape, the alligator does not merely drop its lower jaw but raises its head and upper jaw. The teeth are used for seizing and holding prey—not chewing.

STOMACH. Because an alligator cannot chew, its stomach has two parts—a muscular gizzard and a digestive section. The gizzard's grinding of food is aided by swallowing hard objects.

HEART. Blood passes from the right ventricle through the pulmonary artery for oxygenation by the lungs; it returns through the left atrium to left ventricle, and is pumped out to the body.

SCALES. The alligator's armor is composed of horny scales, each developing on its own and replaced by layers from below. Those shielding the back and tail have bony plates beneath them.

blood. Its respiratory system is better. The nostrils are separated from the mouth by a hard palate. When the alligator swallows a struggling victim there is no danger that a desperate kick will penetrate the roof of its mouth and damage its brain. The alligator has well-developed lungs in comparison to the more primitive saclike structure of snakes. It has the most highly developed brain of any reptile, and is one of the few to have its teeth firmly set in its jaws.

On the other hand, the alligator lacks a well-developed Jacobson's organ, which means that its ability to detect tastes and odors is not nearly so acute as a snake's. It has the well-developed digestive system which works so efficiently for all reptiles, but lacks a bladder, although most turtles and lizards have one. Its ammoniac kidney wastes, along with intestinal wastes, pass through a chamber called the cloaca which opens to the outside of the body.

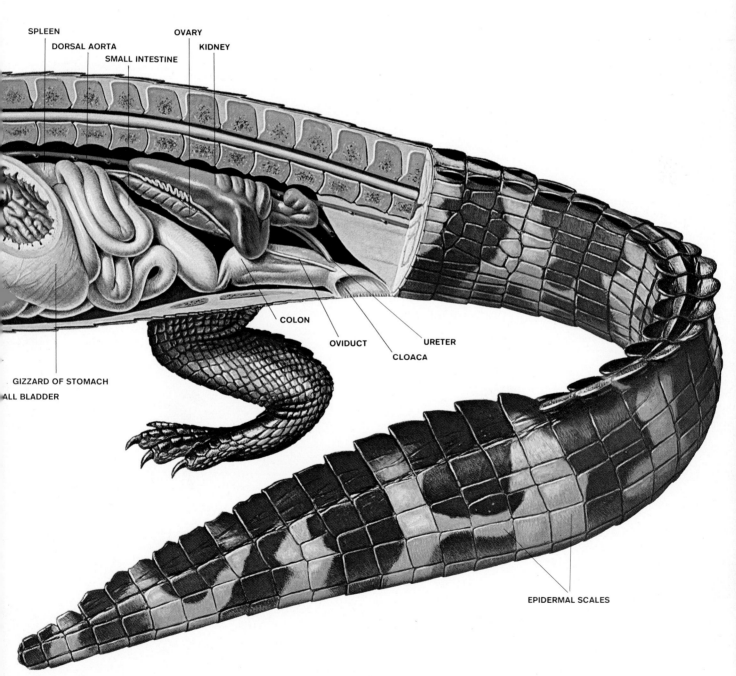

SPLEEN
DORSAL AORTA
SMALL INTESTINE
OVARY
KIDNEY
COLON
OVIDUCT
URETER
CLOACA
GIZZARD OF STOMACH
ALL BLADDER
EPIDERMAL SCALES

The Tenacious Turtles

Clumsy object that it is, the shell has helped ensure the survival of the turtles for 175 million years. Today it is still worn by all species, although it has been modified to suit a variety of environments. Sea turtles, for example, have jettisoned much of their shell bone and are among the fastest-moving of modern reptiles. Land turtles have thinned theirs down to make tiptoe locomotion on their elephantine feet less ponderous. Soft-shelled turtles, which live in fresh water, have developed pancake-shaped shells with flexible edges which they use to help bury themselves. Lying hidden in shallow water, waiting for prey, they occasionally crane their long necks to breathe air with their snorkel-like nostrils. Some-

times they remain submerged for several hours, extracting sufficient oxygen from the water they pump in and out of their pharynges. Recent studies have revealed that turtles can survive for long periods without taking in any oxygen from the outside.

Turtles are believed to be quite hard of hearing. Although they have well-developed middle and inner ears, and although some have voices, the latest evidence is that they hear only sounds of low frequency. They rely instead on their skins and shells to pick up vibrations from the ground or water. They can live a year or more without eating. Some females, in the most amazing feat of all, can produce fertilized eggs as long as four years after mating.

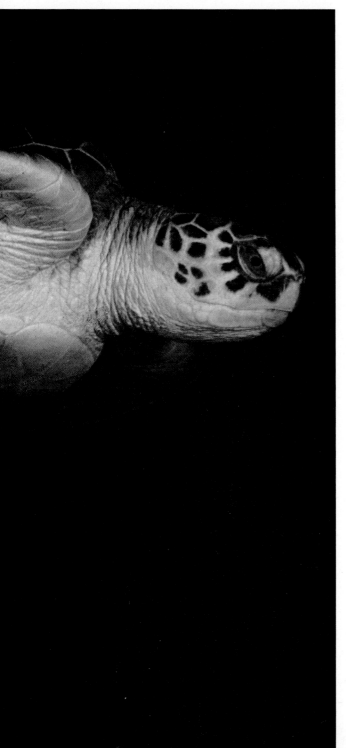

THE DESERT TORTOISE, found in the American Southwest, is protected against loss of moisture by its shell and uses its burrow less as a retreat from danger than as a place to cool off.

THE SPINELESS SOFT-SHELLED TURTLE of the central and southwestern U.S. can hide in the beds of rivers, streams and ponds by shuffling its leathery-skinned shell into sand or silt.

A HAWKSBILL AND A GREEN TURTLE, dwelling in the warm seas, show aquatic adaptations—lightweight shells and paddle-like legs. They swim with birdlike flaps of their front flippers.

21

THE GAVIAL OF INDIA, WITH A RECORDED MAXIMUM LENGTH OF 21.5 FEET, HAS THE NARROWEST SNOUT OF ANY CROCODILIAN AND USES IT

THE AFRICAN CROCODILE, one of the largest of crocodilians, grows 16 feet long. The adult feeds on fishes, mammals and other reptiles, including its young—and is a notorious man-killer.

The Hulking Crocodilians

The crocodilians—the heavily armored crocodiles, alligators and gavials—are the largest of the modern reptiles and the last surviving reptilian descendants of the stock that also produced the dinosaurs. Although somewhat clumsy out of water, they are superbly equipped for living in it. They are strong swimmers, and experts at drifting along on the surface, submerged except for their bulging eyes and nostrils, their long flat jaws not even making a ripple in the water as they stalk turtles, swimming birds and fishes. The larger crocodiles can sometimes get close enough to animals on shore to sweep them—and humans—into deep water with their tails. Crocodilians have valves in their ears and nostrils to keep water out. Because their mouths lack lips and thus do not shut completely, two palatal flaps cover gullet and windpipe during dives.

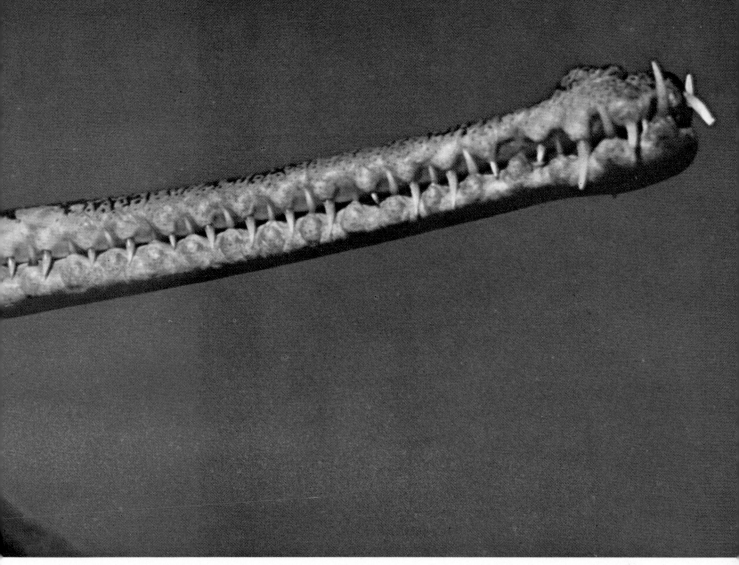

TO MAKE SIDESWIPES AT FISHES. DESPITE ITS OVER-ALL FIERCE LOOK, IT IS A TIMID ANIMAL AND USUALLY RETREATS AT THE SIGHT OF MAN

THE SOUTH AMERICAN CAIMAN, a 6-to-12-foot relative of the mild-mannered American alligator, is the fiercest biter of the crocodilians, and even as a hatchling will display its close-set teeth. It is also the noisiest, with a repertoire of sounds ranging from growls and croaks to snorts and snuffles. During the mating season or when wounded, it lets out thunderous roars.

The Agile Snakes

All 2,700 kinds of snakes tend to look alike—long, squirmy and legless. But despite this superficial resemblance, they show just as much variability of form as their ancestors the lizards do. They range in size from the five inches of a burrowing snake no thicker than a goose quill to the 30 feet of an Asian python over 300 pounds in weight. And with these variations go others—environmental adaptations such as the prehensile tails of many of the arboreal snakes, or skin colors and patterns that match or blend with the surroundings. The amazing thing about snakes is that being legless has not proven a hindrance to locomotion, but an enhancement, making them extremely agile. Some snakes can even outdistance a man in brush or over rough ground.

THE EYELASH VIPER, a poisonous snake of Central America, can wind its prehensile tail several times around a branch and grab at birds with its open mouth while dangling in the air.

THE GREEN TREE SNAKE, colored to blend with Central America's foliage, reaches a length of four feet, but is so slender it can slither along branches without weighing them down.

THE BOA CONSTRICTOR, one of the most beautiful snakes, has a skin pattern harmonizing with shadowy jungle backgrounds. Dark stripes disrupt the head outline, and one disguises the eye.

25

THE KOMODO MONITORS of Indonesia, the largest, heaviest lizards, grow to 10 feet and weigh up to 300 pounds. They occasionally catch small deer or pigs and can swallow them whole.

The Dexterous Lizards

There are about 3,000 species and subspecies of lizards, and though they differ in many ways, they have one habit in common—all shed their skins. Adults molt once every month or so, during the months in which they are active, and unlike snakes, most do not shuffle off their epidermis in one piece, but in patches or even a scale at a time. The banded gecko below rips off its old skin with its mouth and swallows the strips. And to peel its feet, it yanks at each digit as though removing a tight glove.

THE BANDED GECKO OF THE SOUTHWESTERN U.S. BELONGS TO A FAMILY OF AGILE LIZARDS THAT IS MOST PREVALENT IN THE TROPICS. THIS LIZARD

MOLOCH HORRIDUS, named after an ancient god propitiated by child sacrifice, is covered with stubby spines and has two knobs over its eyes, which increase the size of its head. But despite its fearsome name, this Australian lizard is only eight inches long, moves slowly and deliberately, and subsists on a diet of ants, lapping up from 1,000 to 1,500 at a single meal.

COMES OUT ONTO THE DESERT FLOOR AT NIGHT TO HUNT INSECTS AND TWITCHES ITS TAIL IN CATLIKE FASHION JUST BEFORE LUNGING AT ITS PREY

A LEGLESS LIZARD from Florida so resembles an earthworm in both form and locomotion that it is often mistaken for one. Blind and without ear openings, it tunnels through damp soil, where it feeds on ants and termites. When exposed under a log, the foot-long worm lizard may slide back into the burrow tailfirst or use the callused, blunt end of its tail to plug the opening.

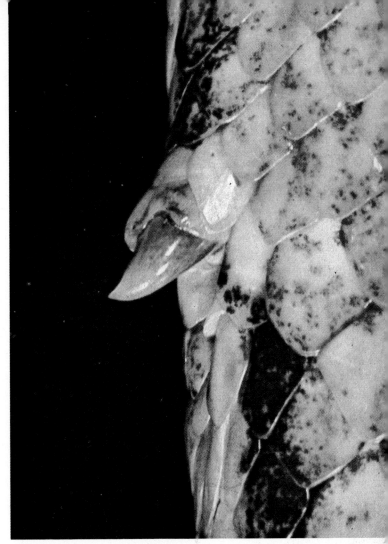

A TINY SPUR, one of two located on each side of an anaconda's vent, is a vestigial leg. The male uses these movable spurs to scratch—and probably stimulate—the female during courtship.

Snakes with "Legs," Lizards Without

Lizards are thought of as having legs and snakes as being legless, but this is not always strictly true. Such snakes as the anaconda, the boa constrictor and the python have vestigial hind legs which they no longer use for locomotion but can still move freely. The worm lizards, with the exception of three species, lack limbs, having lost them in the process of becoming burrowers. They live underground, mainly in the tropics, and tunnel through the earth with their heads. Their skulls are specialized for the task, with brain cases that are almost entirely enclosed and snouts that are often shovel-like, as in the Florida worm lizard at left. Other results of life underground include a soft, pale skin folded into rings, shielded eyes reduced in size, a short tail and a left lung much bigger than the right one.

THE HEAD OF THE AJOLOTE, SMALL IN COMPARISON TO THE THICK BODY, HAS TINY EYES BENEATH THE SKIN AND IS WITHOUT EXTERNAL EARS

A Rare, Two-Legged Lizard

The ajolote, the two-legged worm lizard of Mexico's Baja California, is one of the Western Hemisphere's rarest reptiles. Until recently, when 11 wriggling specimens were presented to the San Diego Zoo, little more was known about it than that it lived underground in burrows and came out only at night. Its stout, clawed feet suggested that it might be able to crawl overland.

Just why the ajolote and two related Mexican species should have front legs, unlike all other leg-less worm lizards, no one is yet able to say. Some authorities suspect that these three species are the least specialized of their family and therefore still in the evolutionary process of reducing and eventually losing their limbs completely. The ajolote uses its legs principally for burrowing in the ground, and though they are only a twentieth of its total length, they still help it a bit in crawling over hard surfaces, with additional thrust supplied by serpentine or caterpillar movements of the trailing body.

MOLELIKE CLAWS of the ajolote are used for digging hard-packed soil, but when the earth is soft they are folded against the body and the blunt head does much of the work, twisting from side to side in an almost circular motion and bulldozing forward. The soft skin covering the legs and the underside of the body is so transparent that the blood vessels often show through.

Lone Survivor of the Past

Sole living representative of the rhynchocephalians, a once widespread group of "beak-headed" reptiles, the tuatara has managed to hang on for 200 million years with only minor evolutionary changes in its skeleton. When it first came to the attention of scientists in 1831, it was identified as a lizard, which it superficially resembles, and a quarter of a century passed before a study of its anatomy revealed its uniqueness. Today, with its range limited to 20 small islands in New Z. and, the tuatara is the subject of extensive research and attempts are being made to find out why it did not disappear ages ago along with all its relatives.

The tuatara grows at a slow rate and probably does not reach sexual maturity until it is at least 20 years old. This would seem to make it one of the longest-lived of animals, and suggests that some of the full-grown males may be over 100 years old. Its eggs are believed to be fertilized nearly a year before being laid and take about 15 months to hatch —much longer than those of most other reptiles.

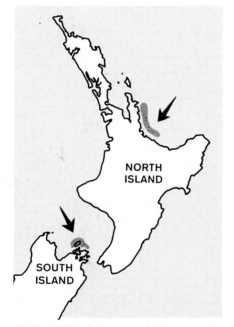

LAST HOME of the tuatara is two groups of very small New Zealand islands shown here by arrows and areas in solid color.

A BRIGHT-EYED TUATARA emerges from a hole under the roots of a small tree. Often the tuatara shares a petrel's burrow with the bird itself—and sometimes with the bird's eggs or young.

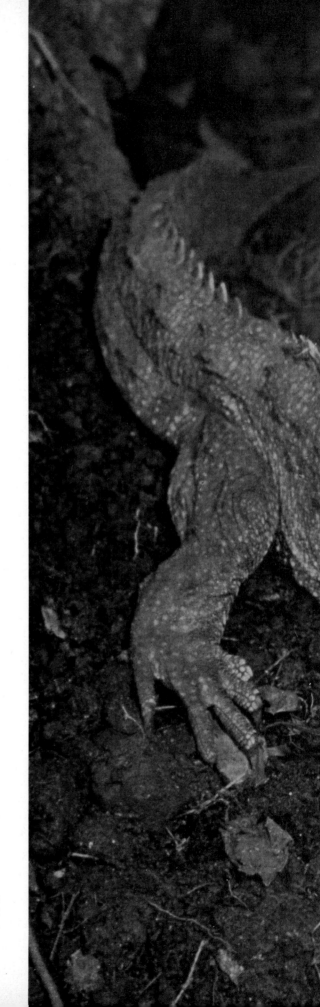

2

The Golden Age
of Reptiles

No student of the history of life on earth will deny that the coming of the reptiles was one of the great events. As the first truly terrestrial verte-brates, the early reptiles not only filled out the faunal picture for their own time in arresting ways, but they also set the stage for later dramatic happen-ings like the rise of the dinosaurs, the beginnings of birds and the age-long evolution of the mammal line.

The reptiles went ashore during the Permian, more than 250 million years ago. There was growing opportunity in the Permian land, and by a surprising twist of history, the reptile ancestors had already evolved equipment to take advantage of the opportunity and become the first terrestrial pioneers. During the time of the coal forests, land vegetation had become well developed. Ferns, seed ferns and their kin covered the low-lying land, the energy of the sun was being caught by chlorophyll, insects had made their appearance and food was wasting on the shore. It was almost certainly the insects as a source of animal food that attracted the reptile ancestors living harassed lives at the rim of the land. If one had to work out this bit of paleontology by logic, one would prob-ably do it this way: the insects were there, vertebrate life was under competitive

BY THEIR HIPS
WE SHALL KNOW THEM

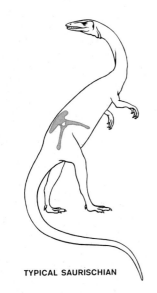

TYPICAL SAURISCHIAN

*Although the two dinosaurs shown here
have a close external resemblance to each
other, they actually represent two distinct
groups: the saurischians and the ornithischians. All dinosaurs belonged to one
group or the other, and they are classified
today by the kind of hipbones they had.
The saurischian hips were quite like those
of even more primitive reptile ancestors.
The more specialized ornithischians developed heavier, stronger hipbones which
were particularly well adapted to a four-
legged gait, although each group contained
both bipedal and four-footed members.*

TYPICAL ORNITHISCHIAN

and predatory pressure in the sea, so some of the shallow-water vertebrates, seeking food and refuge ashore, gradually acquired legs, lungs, scales and the shelled egg, and thus developed at last into land reptiles which were able to forage for insects in the forest.

The process, of course, was not quite that flowing and easily traced. There is a good deal of controversy among experts about the order in which the separate innovations appeared and what immediate selective advantage was gained in each case. One fact is clear, however. Of all the adaptations that fitted the vertebrates into their increasingly refined roles on land, none was more funda-mental than the reptilian egg.

Most people, thinking of an egg, think of a bird; but they are being led astray by seeing eggs mainly at breakfast. The birds did not invent the shelled egg, they inherited it, and it has undergone no important evolution in their pos-session. The first shelled land eggs were reptilian, and the reptiles were rep-tiles only when they had evolved such an egg. The old riddle, "which came first, the hen or the egg," is just whimsey when the hen is a bird. But applied to reptiles the question is valid, and paleontologists are still getting testy with each other trying to answer it.

THE reptiles came from amphibian ancestors. The egg of the usual amphib-ian is almost naked, enclosed only by a jelly envelope. The jelly supports each egg separately in the mass, keeps out small invaders and discourages pre-dation by larger animals, but it gives almost no protection against drying up. A typical frog egg on land on a clear day will quickly wither. Thus, no matter how far the adult frog may be able to move from water in the course of its own daily activities, when it comes time to provide new frogs most species have to go home to the water. The songs of male frogs all over the world calling the females to the ponds show how strong the obligation is.

The egg as the reptiles developed it—which was essentially as we know it today—had no such limitation. Its smooth shell tightly shut in white and yolk. Like any egg, as it incubated it got more complex inside, and the complexity was not just in the forming body of the new animal but also in the structures re-quired to keep the embryo alive in its shell—to keep it supported, fed, un-poisoned and unasphyxiated.

The structures that did this are known as the embryonic membranes. They were evolved by the reptiles and kept by the birds; and, with modifications, they also serve as embryonic structures of the mammals. Because they occur both in the shelled egg and in the uterine development of the mammal, all three higher vertebrate classes—mammals, reptiles and birds—are collectively called amniotes. The name refers to one of the embryonic membranes, the amnion, which shuts in a fluid in which the embryo is able to go on leading an essentially aquatic existence as it develops. A yolk sac is stalked from the belly region of the embryo, and just behind its attachment is that of the allantois, another sac which partly fills the space between the amnion and a third mem-brane, the chorion, which lies just beneath the shell. The allantois receives and stores embryonic waste, serving as a sort of bladder. It also has blood vessels that pick up oxygen that passes through the shell and conduct it to the embryo. The shell cuts down evaporation, but it is porous and does not wall the em-bryo off completely. It shuts out prying small animals, for example, but not the oxygen the embryo requires to live.

For the embryo to thrive, such an egg must be kept warm and not too dry, and must never be submerged for long in the water. Thus the shelled egg, laid on land, is a kind of private sequestered pool in which a tender, beginning reptile can go through its perishable stages in much the same environment its ancestors lived in. The egg itself is a terrestrial adaptation, but the animal it harbors is still aquatic.

The shelled egg is thus the essence of the reptile. No amount of protection of any animal's adult stages will allow real pioneering on shore if the embryos remain unprotected. The adult can save its juices with scales, or it can move about to damp places to avoid drying up. But an embryo starts out as a helpless cell, almost without structure and without any capacity for movement at all, and it must be protected if it is to survive.

One of the frustrating features of the fossil record of vertebrate history is that it shows so little about the evolution of reptiles during their earliest days, when the shelled egg was developing. There are three fundamental body features that the earliest land vertebrates had, and it would be very nice if we could draw a neat, clear, logical picture of their development. These features are: legs, lungs, and a connection between nostril and pharynx that allowed animals to breathe with their mouths shut. Unfortunately for logic, these things were not started by reptiles, nor even by the earlier amphibians. We must go even farther back, to the fishes, to find their beginnings. In trying to account for this, alternate explanations come to mind. Either the fishes that had the structures used them for some hidden purpose lost in time; or their bearers actually did use them for what seems the obvious purpose of such an adaptation—going out on land. The latter is what paleontologists believe. The old lung-bearing, nose-breathing, stalk-finned fishes, known as Crossopterygii, remained fishes, but they apparently acquired the new adaptations in order to survive in the uncertainty of a shore-water environment that was subject to periods of drying up. Alfred S. Romer of Harvard some time ago made the ingenious suggestion that the first ventures ashore were perhaps not hunting trips, but more likely mud-slogging hegiras out of drying-up pools in search of better water. That is to say, the land-life equipment was at first used in search of ways to stay *in* the water rather than get out of it, at a time when the water was disappearing.

THERE is logic in this argument. There was probably no well-developed spread of truly terrestrial insects in Devonian times. Because the ancestral vertebrates are believed to have been carnivorous, they would have found slim pickings on shore until well toward the end of the Carboniferous, so it is hardly likely that food motivated these first terrestrial adaptations in the fishes in these earliest, pre-insect times.

And yet some of the early vertebrates did somehow become land-adapted. Over a great span of Paleozoic time we find developments occurring in four kinds of creatures, and it is logical to try to string them together into some kind of evolutionary sequence. First there were the stalk-finned fishes, then scaled amphibia known as labyrinthodonts, then some kinds of semiaquatic reptiles, and finally true land reptiles. These surely all belong to a single bloodline, but they overlapped in time, and the evolution to a finished land reptile was certainly not a smoothly progressive adaptive process going hand in hand with a gradual movement into the land. On the contrary, like most things in the long, slow, millennia-consuming process of evolution, it had fits and starts, blind alleys, repetitions and reversals. One theory even holds that the shelled egg evolved in a still-aquatic animal as a protection against the hazards of larval life in the water—and no doubt the teeming shore waters of Carboniferous seas and lagoons had predators aplenty to stimulate such a move.

There is another theory about how the reptiles got started and brought out the shelled egg. Coleman and Olive Goin have recently suggested that the great advance occurred among creatures living in mountainous regions, where standing water was scarce, streams ran fast, and eggs laid in them were in danger of being swept away by the current. Aquatic eggs are usually fertilized outside the body of the female. A typical frog—presumably still following the pattern of the primitive amphibians—lays her eggs at the same time the male releases sperm into the surrounding water. Each egg is fertilized by the winner of a little race among the sperm. In fast water there might be no winners—the sperm might all be swept away, even if the eggs were not. Internal fertilization and a land egg go together nicely, because land eggs have shells which make external fertilization impossible since the sperm cannot get through the shell. So the Goins propose that both the shelled egg and the behavioral pattern that allows it to be fertilized inside the body of the female before the shell is put on may have been an outcome of evolution of ancestral reptiles under pressure to develop ways to survive in rapid water in mountainous terrain.

THIS theory, of course, is as speculative as any of the others, but it follows the view prevailing today that both the primary anatomical adaptations and the shelled egg were acquired while the bearers were still in the water. And speculate we must, since neither behavior nor eggs fossilize well. But despite the trouble we have timing the separate steps toward the land, it is clear that before the Carboniferous was over, the "stem" reptiles, the cotylosaurs, had arisen. Their name derives from the fact that all later reptiles stem from them. During the Permian they diverged and set the stage for a number of important evolutionary events. They gave rise to the turtles, to the now extinct ichthyosaurs (of which more will be said in the chapter on water reptiles), to the mammal-like reptiles, from which our own line has come, and to the archosaurs, the fated creatures which would give rise to the main figures of the Age of Reptiles. For it was these archosaurs—the name means "ruling reptiles"—that produced, among others, the dinosaurs.

Subjectively speaking, as a sort of symbol of the inborn exuberance of protoplasm, no event of earth history can match the flowering of the dinosaurs. What man is doing is pretty fancy, but man is a single, separate sort of beast, not to be compared to the dinosaurs, which were a fantastically diverse group, all of them pure, authentic animals operating under the strong hand of natural selection. To put reptiles into a decent perspective I shall have to dwell for a little on the dinosaurs. Everybody should learn about them anyway. The study of dinosaurs is good for the human soul.

The dinosaurs first appeared in the Triassic, some 200 million years ago. At the beginning they were not the giants one thinks of, but were mostly small, some no bigger than a chicken. Like a chicken, they were bipedal, walking or hopping about on their two hind legs. Though later some showed four-legged adaptations, this two-leggedness was from the start an unmistakable and typical sign of the dinosaur line.

Toward the end of the Triassic, two great orders of dinosaurs began to take shape. Their main difference was in the structure of the pelvis. The first to develop, the Saurischia, eventually came to include four-legged as well as two-

TWO MESOZOIC FLIERS

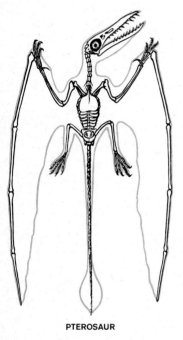

PTEROSAUR

Although no reptiles can fly today, some did in the past. This long-tailed Rhamphorhynchus was one of these reptiles which took to the air some 180 million years ago. A big-jawed, toothy creature, it had an extremely elongated finger on each forelimb, providing a frame for its featherless wing. The other clawed fingers protruded for climbing. The tail ended in a rudder, aiding stability in flight. It had weak legs, probably walked little and cruised low over the water in search of its prey.

legged members, and herbivores as well as carnivores. The other, the Ornithischia, likewise had some four-legged forms but all ornithischians fed on plants.

The biggest dinosaurs were the giant amphibious saurischians, such as *Brontosaurus*, *Diplodocus* and *Brachiosaurus*. The last named weighed some 50 tons and was the biggest land vertebrate that ever lived. In the skeletons of such animals the crushing point of bone seems to have been approached and they must have spent most of their lives partly supported by water. The most terrible carnivore was also of this order—the predaceous *Tyrannosaurus*, which reached a length of nearly 50 feet and stood, in a bipedal crouch, some 19 feet high.

During the ensuing 50 million years of the Jurassic period it was the saurischians that flourished and predominated. In the Cretaceous period that followed it, however, great changes came over both the landscape and the dinosaur fauna in it. There was widespread mountain-building and the easy old tropical weather in most regions gave way to more temperate climates. Much of the tropical and subtropical vegetation was killed off, the flowering plants evolved and spread, and by the end of the age forest and swamp were essentially modern. In this new Cretaceous landscape the herbivorous Ornithischia flourished. If the Saurischia included the most ponderous land animals the world has known and the most terrible carnivores, the Ornithischia were surely the most bizarre. The peak of dinosaur evolution came in the Cretaceous, in the duckbill, horned and armored dinosaurs, the iguanodonts and plated dinosaurs. Some of these browsed in woods fundamentally similar to those we know today.

A Cretaceous event dwarfed by the towering phenomenon of the dinosaurs but important to the future of reptiles was the appearance of the snakes. The question of their ancestry is one of the most controversial problems in herpetology. They obviously came from lizards, but how? Two ideas have been advanced. The first one is that the forebears of snakes were legless lizards. This would explain the present leglessness of snakes. Equally suggestive is the difference between the modern snake eye and the lizard eye. The former gives some indication of having degenerated during its long period as an organ of the primitive burrowers, and then having undergone a burst of secondary evolution into a useful organ of sight again when its owners, the modern snakes, began spending most of their time above ground.

INGENIOUS as these ideas are, they are disregarded by some fossil experts who have discovered significant kinships between snakes and several extinct groups of aquatic lizards, the aigialosaurs, the dolichosaurs and the mosasaurs. These, along with such surviving types as the monitors, the Gila monster and a little-known Bornean lizard, make up a group called the Platynota. Unfortunately all Platynota are, or were, either giant aquatic animals or provided with good functional legs.

Thus, the two prevalent theories of snake origin fail to fit together into a clear pattern of snake history. It would help if a subterraneous, blind, limbless monitor or mosasaur could be found, but so far none has turned up. Whatever the derivation of snakes may have been, and whatever the initial value of limblessness to the early snakes, there can be no doubt that an efficient new locomotor system has taken the place of the lost limbs. When they abandoned the four-point limb support for their bodies, the early snakes also removed limits to their lengths. They allowed serpentine movements to replace footwork and this laid the groundwork for other modifications as well. Constriction—killing of prey by squeezing it—is an example. Another is the series of tree-climbing adap-

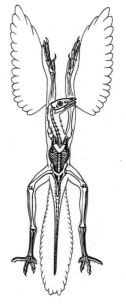

ARCHAEOPTERYX

The crow-sized Archaeopteryx, an ancient bird which lived toward the end of the era of flying reptiles, possessed many characteristics of the reptiles from which it sprang. Like the birds, Archaeopteryx was feathered and had strong hind limbs with claws adapted for perching. But it had a toothed, reptilian beak, claws on its forelimbs and a reptilian tail. Fossil remains indicate that the animal had a weak jaw and small teeth and, unlike the pterosaurs, probably fed on plants, insects and slugs.

tations of arboreal species, and the concurrent advantages of having a long body that can be made to look like a twig or branch. Also, the loss of the limbs and girdles and the reduction of the cross section of the body permitted snakes to go into places like narrow caves and rock crevices that would be closed to a four-legged animal of similar chest expansion. And for aquatic snakes the ability to swim by passing waves of undulation backward along the body made the loss of the limbs and lengthening of the body not merely inconsequential, but actually a gain.

To the modern snakes the lack of legs is not by any means a handicap to locomotion. Although for sheer speed over smooth ground most men can move faster than most snakes, this is not true in cluttered places. Let the landscape be wooded, rough or scrubby and the snake a whip snake or racer, and a whole posse of men will be left behind in the chase.

Aerial locomotion—sustained flight—first achieved by the insects in the coal forests millions of years before, was evolved twice during the Age of Reptiles. The first venture was that of the pterosaurs, often called pterodactyls, in the Lower Jurassic. These were light-bodied archosaurs which took to the air on leathery wings stretched by their finger bones. The pterosaurs no doubt began as gliders, and some may never have acquired the ability to keep up sustained flapping flight, but others certainly did. It is believed that some pterosaurs fed on the wing, dipping fish out of the sea like modern sea birds. The biggest of them, *Pteranodon*, had a wingspread of more than 20 feet.

In the Jurassic, some 150 million years ago, the reptiles made a completely different approach to the problem of flight. This other plan is revealed in some famous fossils found in Germany. The oldest representative of this other kind of aerialist is known as *Archaeopteryx*. Three skeletons have been found. One is now in the British Museum, another in Erlangen and the third and best-preserved is in the Berlin Museum. The skeletal structure is essentially that of a small, spry-looking dinosaur. But by vast good luck the faithful preservation in the fine-grained Jurassic stone shows the clear imprints of feathers. A feather means a bird. Feathers, obviously derived from the scales of reptiles, are the most distinctive feature of birds, and almost their only evolutionary innovation.

There are only a few obvious differences between birds and reptiles. To answer the demands of flight, birds have achieved a constant body temperature and a metabolic rate higher than that of reptiles. For lightness some of the bones have become hollow. A breastbone has developed for attachment of the flying muscles, and bones of the forelimb have been lost or bound together to support the wing along its leading edge. The teeth and the long reptilian tail are gone. Looked at with these differences in mind, *Archaeopteryx* is a wonderful example of an intermediate creature. Its jaws were toothed, its tail was long, its breastbone was weak and all its bones were solid. Its power of flight was surely feeble; but it had feathers, and it stands as a beautifully explicit link and sign of kinship between the nightingale and the crocodile. Archbishop Ussher himself, gazing upon *Archaeopteryx*, would embrace Darwinism, and would know at once where the birds came from.

The record of the derivation of mammals from reptiles is both far longer and far more detailed than the history of birds—and also, unfortunately, it is far less clear. It begins with the pelycosaurs of the late Carboniferous—a group not far removed from the old stem reptiles. From these there radiated a great array of types known as mammal-like reptiles, and during the late Paleozoic

ALIKE BUT UNRELATED

OSTRICH DINOSAUR

OSTRICH

Many of the reptiles that appeared during the heyday of the dinosaurs were well adapted to ways of life that later were taken over by modern reptiles, mammals and birds. Since their habits were similar it is not surprising that their shapes were too. The eight-foot-tall ostrich dinosaur, for example, was an omnivorous browser of open plains. Like the modern ostrich, it had a toothless beak and powerful legs.

and early Mesozoic these creatures were the dominant vertebrates on the land.

There is no missing link between mammals and reptiles, nor any single fossil type which, as *Archaeopteryx* does for birds, stands out clearly as half reptile, half mammal. If each mammalian feature could be traced to its point of origin, we might hope to put a finger on the first mammals. As it is, the case rests mostly on bones and teeth, and relying on such skeletal characters alone, we only see the ancestral forms slowly acquiring the skeleton and dentition that today we associate with mammals. We can only deduce the scheduling of the less solid attributes not susceptible to preservation in the rocks.

Fortunately there are good clear differences in the skeletons of reptiles and mammals. One such is the structure of the jaw joint. Two bones enter this joint in both mammals and reptiles, but they are different bones in the two animals. Furthermore, while in the mammal the lower jaw is a single bone, in the ancestral reptiles several bones are involved. Fossils from the late Triassic show various stages of reduction of jawbones, and a number of other traits that we now associate with mammals made their appearance at the same time.

By the Jurassic there were real mammals in the world. They were all small insecure-looking creatures, and when we consider the kinds of beasts they shared the earth with we may justifiably wonder how they were able to hold on at all. There could be no better illustration of the vagaries of extinction and survival. After thundering about for 80 million years the dinosaurs have gone, and the hairy, feisty, rat-small creatures that cowered about their feet have inherited the earth.

The Age of Reptiles is an ideal time from which to draw graphic illustrations of the three great evolutionary processes: extinction, survival and adaptive radiation, the last being the tendency for a stock of living things to evolve in such a way as to exploit all the available opportunities of its environment. From their modest beginnings in the Triassic, the dinosaur line spread and split and sent out adaptive versions of itself into endless specialized roles and niches. The whole spectrum of Mesozoic life, furthermore, shows a similar trend. But because the adaptive radiation of dinosaurs was the most spectacular show put on by vertebrate animals prior to the hydrogen bomb, the completely unexplained cutting off of all dinosaur lines in the Cretaceous is one of the most impressive cases of extinction that we know about. And when extinction happens to a vast, noisy, exuberant and seemingly forever-entrenched crowd like the dinosaurs, it demands an explanation. But though a great deal of thought has been given to the matter, it still remains largely an impressive mystery.

MANY theories have been advanced to account for the immense dying of the dinosaurs. Some of them are almost persuasive, some seem pretty desperate. Without going into the merits of these, it can be said that this great anomaly remains to confound them all: it was not a single species of animal that disappeared so unaccountably, it was several *orders* of reptiles. It was a broad spectrum of animal life occupying all sorts of environments and habitats. Some of the creatures were tiny, some gigantic, some ordinary reptiles, some among the most bizarre animals that ever lived. If too-great size, and thus too-great surface-to-volume ratio in times of rising temperatures killed off the sauropods, then what struck down the pterosaurs, most of which were wispy aerialists that lived in wholly different ways? If mammals ate up the eggs of the terrestrial dinosaurs, what plagued the live-bearing ichthyosaurs that ranged the open seas? And so it goes. The fact is, the event has not been accounted for. We

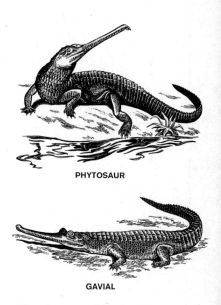

PHYTOSAUR

GAVIAL

There is an astonishingly close resemblance between the Triassic phytosaur, which became extinct 200 million years ago, and the gavial, a kind of crocodile found in Asia today. Both lived in swamps and on muddy riverbanks. Both were ferocious carnivores with long-toothed jaws for snatching fishes. But the phytosaur's nostrils were just in front of its eyes, while the gavial's are at the end of its snout.

PLACODUS

WALRUS

The eight-foot-long Placodus was also a Triassic reptile. Its stoutish body, short neck and tail and paddlelike limbs resembled those of the modern walrus, a mammal. Like the walrus, it was a marine animal that dove down to the bottom in search of shellfish which it crushed with its strong jaws and teeth. Although it lacked the canine tusks of the walrus, its front teeth were used as efficient nippers.

know only that a vast and far-flung fauna was wiped out and replaced by a fauna of mammals, leaving the world of today with only remnants of the once-great orders.

The dinosaurs were by no means the only Mesozoic reptiles that burgeoned and spread and then became extinct. Of the others, some made ventures into alleys that went quickly blind; others, like the ichthyosaurs and plesiosaurs were successful radiations that endured far longer than modern mammals have been on earth. Most of them were stocks that went back into the sea, and more will be said of them in the chapter on water reptiles. The grand days of the crocodilians were the Mesozoic days, when one kind reached a length of 50 feet; and crocodile architecture was paralleled in astonishing detail by that of the phytosaurs, a completely separate branch from the Permian reptile stem. The crocodiles hung on; the phytosaurs, although in their own time they appeared to be just as promising, are gone, for reasons we do not know, and in all likelihood never will.

IT pays a creature like man to keep in mind the vast time spans of the "unsuccessful" lives of these cutoff bloodlines. In evolution, of course, there is nothing novel about lines becoming extinct. Extinction is the rule, and survival the breathtakingly improbable exception. When you look about at the animals and plants on earth today, what you see is the favored few. For every single stock running down into the present, thousands have been cut off. This applies not just to species, but to genera and families, and even to orders. During the Mesozoic, there were times when 16 orders of reptiles lived on earth at one time. Today there are four. One of these, the tuatara, is a single species with a drastically diminished range on a few New Zealand islands. Two of the orders are decadent, and only one, the Squamata, has shown recent evolutionary vigor. In brief, out of the whole teeming array of Mesozoic reptiles, only these stocks, listed here in the order of their branching out from the main reptile stem, remain on earth today:

(1) the mammals, which split off as the mammal-like reptiles in the Permian, some 250 million years ago;

(2) the turtles, which were probably derived during Permian times and were well developed by the Triassic;

(3) the crocodilians, which were derived from Triassic archosaurs;

(4) the tuatara, the only species of its order still alive, which has remained almost unchanged since its origin in Triassic eosuchian stock;

(5) the lizards and the snakes—the lizards having split off in the Upper Triassic, the snakes in the Cretaceous;

(6) the birds, which first appeared in the Jurassic in the intermediate form of *Archaeopteryx* and almost certainly were derived from Triassic archosaurs.

If we had been alive in the Age of Reptiles the great sight would have been the sweep of the deployment—the adaptive radiation of unprecedented types of life into unprecedented ways of living. Today, looking at what remains, we see the lesson of extinction and survival. The whole spirit of the grand, doomed days seems held in the small, cold body of the tuatara on the few chill islets of its dwindled range. Living on as unaccountably as the giants it once lived with died, it creeps out of its burrow in the evening, plods about in the mist to gather crickets to keep the old, small flame of its life alive; then, in the early morning, goes back again into the earth to which it has clung so stubbornly for some 200 million years.

A VIEW OF A 42-FOOT-LONG KRONOSAURUS SKELETON SHOWS THE MASSIVE BONES OF ONE OF THE LARGEST MARINE REPTILES EVER

Days of Doomed Grandeur

Emerging from streams and ponds some 365 million years ago, the reptile ancestors established a beachhead during the Upper Devonian and eventually gave rise to myriad bizarre creatures, from gopher-sized cotylosaurs to the schooner-sized Brontosaurus. While many returned to the water, a few took to the air. But most remained on land to dominate the earth for some 200 million years.

Evolution of Reptiles

The history of reptiles, from their first appearance during the Carboniferous to the present, is traced on this chart. (Each white area represents a major order plotted according to when it first began to flower and how long it lasted.) In addition to the major groups, many short-lived offshoots developed. For reasons of space only two of them, represented by the marine forms Geosaurus and Tylosaurus, have been included here. Solid bars on the chart indicate lines of descent which have been fairly well established by the fossil record. Broken bars are used where the fossil evidence is sketchy.

A striking aspect of reptile history is how, from the primitive cotylosaurs (here represented by Seymouria), these creatures radiated to occupy an enormous variety of niches on land, in the water, and in the air. One group of cotylosaurian descendants that played a profound role in the development of reptiles was the thecodonts, primitive archosaurs. Not only did they give rise to the Ornithischia and Saurischia (popularly called dinosaurs), but also the Pterosauria (flying reptiles) and the Crocodilia. Thecodonts were even related to the ancestral birds. The mammals evolved from another group, the therapsids, shown at lower left.

Another curious fact of reptilian evolution revealed by this chart is the relative suddenness with which order after order disappeared toward the end of the Cretaceous, described as "the time of the great dying."

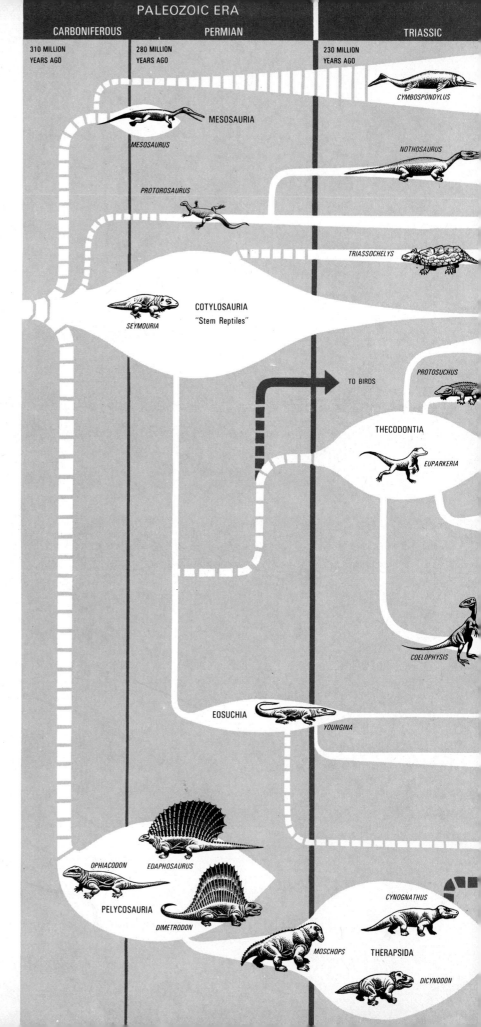

CYMBOSPONDYLUS

MESOSAURIA

MESOSAURUS

NOTHOSAURUS

PROTOROSAURUS

TRIASSOCHELYS

COTYLOSAURIA
"Stem Reptiles"

SEYMOURIA

TO BIRDS

PROTOSUCHUS

THECODONTIA

EUPARKERIA

COELOPHYSIS

EOSUCHIA

YOUNGINA

OPHIACODON   EDAPHOSAURUS

PELYCOSAURIA

DIMETRODON

CYNOGNATHUS

MOSCHOPS   THERAPSIDA

DICYNODON

135 MILLION
YEARS AGO

63 MILLION
YEARS AGO

ONE MILLION
YEARS AGO

OSAURIA

ICHTHYOSAURUS

PLESIOSAURUS

SAUROPTERYGIA

ELASMOSAURUS

TURTLES
200 ± SPECIES

PROTOROSAURIA

CHELONIA

RHAMPHORHYNCHUS

PTEROSAURIA

PTERANODON

CROCODILIA

GEOSAURUS

CROCODILES-
ALLIGATORS
23 SPECIES

STEGOSAURUS   CAMPTOSAURUS   PROTOCERATOPS

LIDOSAURUS

ORNITHISCHIA

ANKYLOSAURUS

TRACHODON

TRICERATOPS

ORNITHOLESTES

SAURISCHIA

TYRANNOSAURUS

BRONTOSAURUS

GORGOSAURUS

TUATARA
1 SPECIES

RHYNCHOCEPHALIA

HOMOEOSAURUS

SQUAMATA

SNAKES
2,700 ± Species

TO MAMMALS

POLYODONTOSAURUS

LIZARDS
3,000 ± SPECIES

TYLOSAURUS

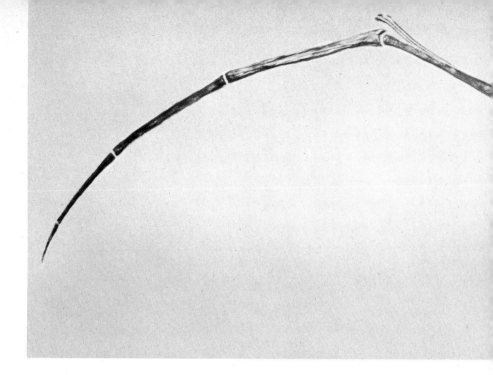

NYCTOSAURUS, a flying reptile, had greatly elongated fourth-finger bones to support its seven-foot-wide membranous wings, and was better adapted to soaring than flapping flight. Although most of its bones were hollow and birdlike, *Nyctosaurus* was neither a bird nor a bird ancestor. In fact, it was competition from the more efficient true birds that probably pushed *Nyctosaurus* and other flying reptiles to their long glide to extinction during the Cretaceous, some 70 million years ago.

Infinite Evolutionary Variety from a Primitive "Stem" Ancestor

The world's great variety of vertebrate life got a major boost from the cotylosaurs, the first, or "stem," reptiles—the most important animals in reptilian history. These humble, ground-hugging creatures gave rise to a multitude of other reptiles, some of which in turn were the ancestors of birds and

DIADECTES, A "STEM" REPTILE AND ONE OF THE FIRST VERTEBRATE HERBIVORES, HAD FLAT GRINDING TEETH FOR MUNCHING FOREST PLANTS

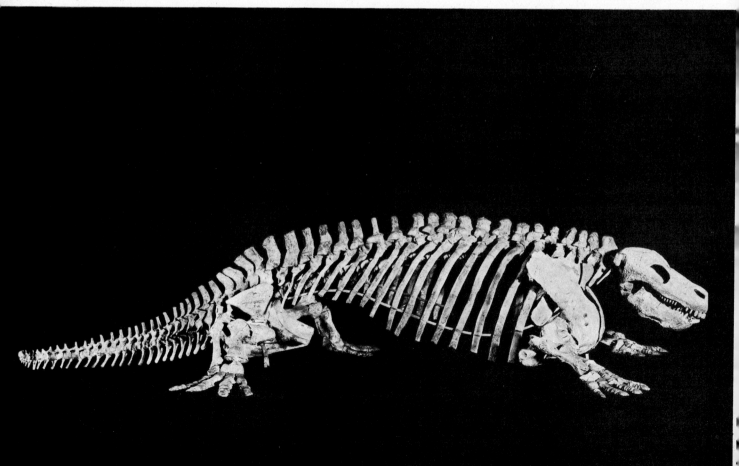

mammals. *Diadectes (below, left)*, with its thick body, short skull and sprawling limbs, was a member of this ancestral stock from which evolved such totally different creatures as *Nyctosaurus (above)*, a pigeon-sized flying reptile with an eagle's wingspread, and *Moschops (below, right)*, a ponderous plant eater.

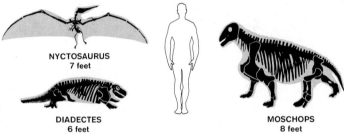

NYCTOSAURUS
7 feet

DIADECTES
6 feet

MOSCHOPS
8 feet

MOSCHOPS, WITH ITS THICK SKULL AND BODY, WAS ONE OF THE EARLY REPTILES TO RAISE ITSELF HIGH AND DEVELOP A MAMMAL-LIKE GAIT

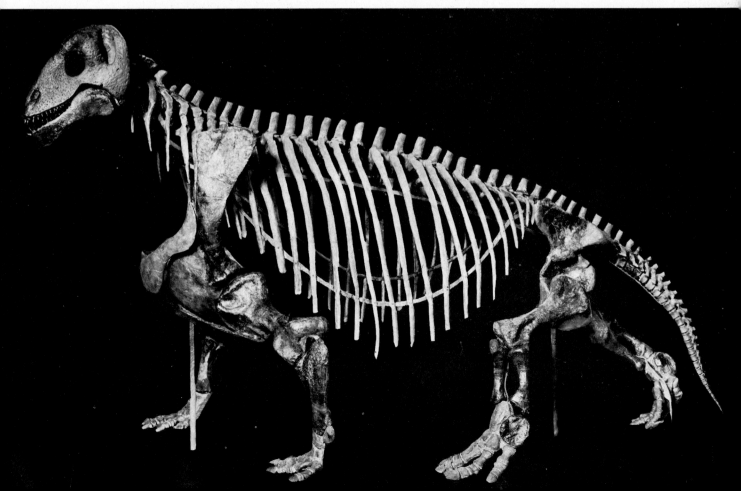

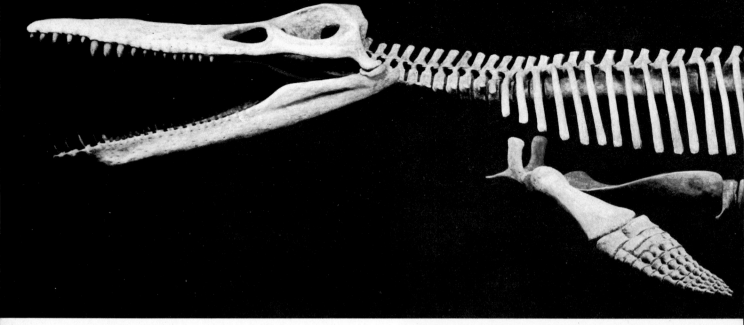

UNEARTHED IN AUSTRALIA, THIS IS THE ONLY MOUNTED SPECIMEN OF KRONOSAURUS, A FRONT VIEW OF WHICH IS SHOWN ON PAGE 43. THIS

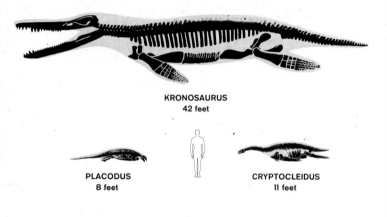

KRONOSAURUS
42 feet

PLACODUS
8 feet

CRYPTOCLEIDUS
11 feet

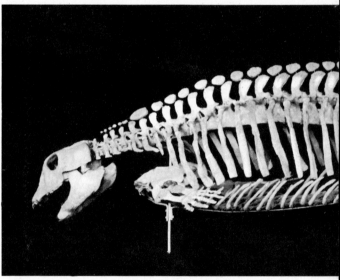

PLACODUS, ONLY EIGHT FEET LONG AND SMALL FOR A MARINE REPTILE,

CRYPTOCLEIDUS, AN 11-FOOT-LONG, SURFACE-SWIMMING PREDATOR OF

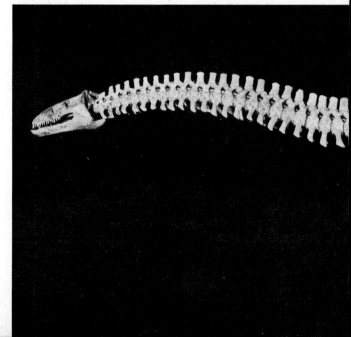

Back to the Sea

After 70 million years of terrestrial life, some reptiles returned to the sea. One group, the sauropterygians shown on these pages, retained many reptilian characteristics, although their bodies became
more streamlined. All the sauropterygians developed
hard rib "baskets" to support their abdomens and
protect their vulnerable undersides from attack.

Prominent among the sauropterygians was an important group called plesiosaurs. One of these was
Kronosaurus (top), a fast-diving predator with huge,
fish-trapping jaws. Another was *Cryptocleidus (bottom)*, which used its long, flexible neck for pluck-
ing victims from passing schools of fish. *Placodus*,
in the middle, was not a plesiosaur; it was a lei-
surely bottom feeder that ground crustaceans to bits
with its mouthful of flat, crushing platelike teeth.

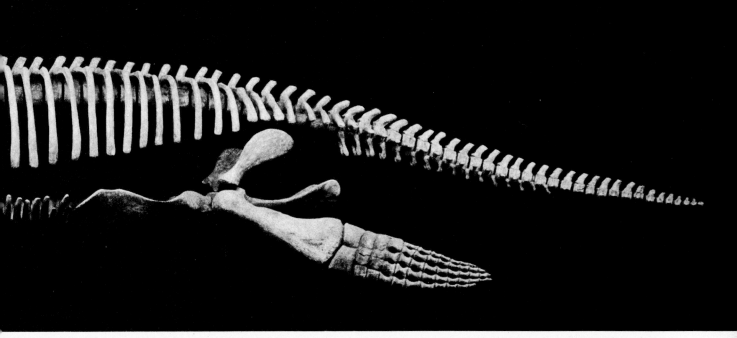

CARNIVORE HAD A NINE-FOOT SKULL AND LARGE LIMB PADDLES. IT MAY HAVE FED ON ITS OWN KIND AS WELL AS ON SMALLER MARINE CREATURES

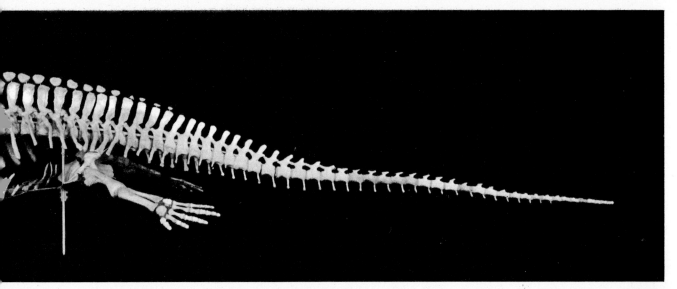

WAS PROBABLY A SLOW SWIMMER. BUT IT MAY HAVE FOUND SOME PROTECTION FROM ARMOR ATTACHED TO NODULES ABOVE ITS VERTEBRAE

THE LATE JURASSIC SEAS, BELONGS TO THE LONG-NECKED SAUROPTERYGIANS, SOME OF WHICH HAD NECKS TWICE THE LENGTH OF THEIR BODIES

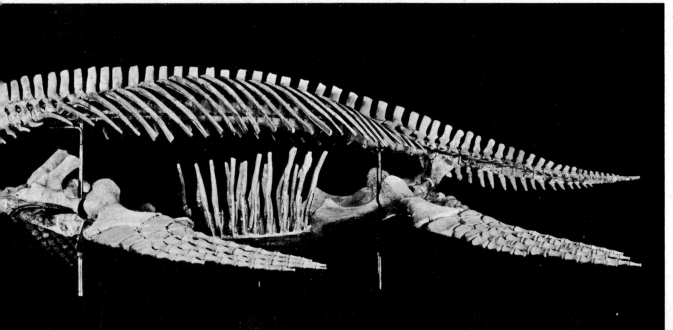

MYSTRIOSAURUS was a nine-foot aquatic reptile from Europe. It belonged to a group of the early crocodilians. Although *Mystriosaurus* lived some 150 million years ago, its fossils show a remarkable anatomical resemblance to crocodilians of today.

Two Orders That Survived

Crocodilians and turtles have remained relatively unchanged for some 150 million years, having survived the mysterious disasters of the Mesozoic which wiped out most of the earth's reptile orders. The crocodilians seem to have parried extinction by adhering to a successful pattern of predatory existence. As long ago as the Jurassic, some primitive crocodilians already resembled, and presumably behaved much like, the later creatures to which they gave rise. One of these was *Mystriosaurus (above)*, which, like its modern counterparts, was armored with rows of bony plates, had a long, powerful jaw and prowled the shallows of tropical coasts.

When the prototypes of modern turtles appeared during the Triassic, they were largely terrestrial. These early creatures had already developed the characteristic turtle shell and had lost most of their teeth, their jaws being enclosed with horny beaks. Among the largest group, the Cryptodira, which appeared during the Cretaceous, there evolved types that could live almost anywhere, in deserts, swamps or open seas, and ate almost anything from leaves to lizards. Such flexibility contributed heavily to their survival. *Archelon (right)* was a seagoing cryptodire with characteristics of some of the modern marine turtles: a tough layer of skin in place of a shell, like the leatherbacks, and the inability to retract its neck completely.

ARCHELON, the largest turtle that ever lived, was almost 11 feet long and 12 feet across at the flippers. The missing hind flipper was probably bitten off by one of the fish or reptile predators that were *Archelon's* competitors in the Cretaceous seas.

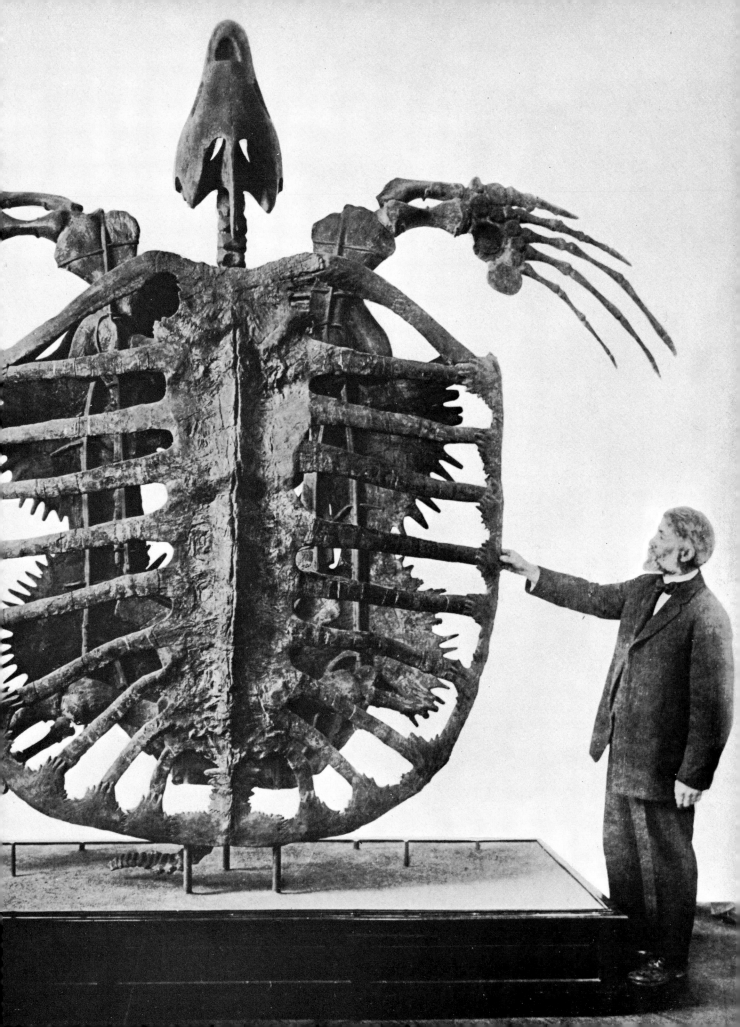

SHELL AND ALL, a caiman lizard of South America chews up a snail, carefully spitting out the fragments of shell *(bottom)* before swallowing their contents. Its large flat teeth are specifically adapted for this task.

3

The Business of Eating

Most animals are at least to some degree shaped by the way they eat. Pursuers of live prey must be quick and agile, rooters and burrowers have special tools to help them find their food. So it is with reptiles. The wide range of their feeding habits is reflected in the great diversity of their appearance. Reptiles, like the other classes of land vertebrates, include both carnivorous and herbivorous members, and there are others that eat almost anything nourishing which the environment affords.

It was not always like that, however. The reptile ancestors were carnivores and originally no doubt were adapted to stalking live prey in the form of insects. Insects are small packages of highly concentrated energy, and for many reptiles they are still the basic food, along with many other invertebrates such as spiders and earthworms. But there are numerous others that have radiated out into the great spectrum of feeding roles that the environment makes profitable. Their feeding adaptations fall into three basic categories: (1) equipment for a herbivorous diet; (2) adaptations making possible the swallowing of big—in some cases enormous—objects; and (3) equipment and behavior adapted to the taking of some one special kind of food—eggs, for instance.

Some insight into the evolutionary history of reptilian feeding habits can be got from the study of their individual development. In the embryonic and larval development of an animal there is often a tendency to repeat, in a crude sort of outline form, the stages of evolution by which the race was produced. This is never a rigid, detailed process of rehashing evolution, but simply a trend in which stages or structures repeat themselves in a broad and general way. Thus, human embryos go through a stage when they have gill-like pouches which hark back to our remote fish ancestors. Similarly, most young reptiles, whatever diet they may choose in later life, begin as insect eaters.

It might, of course, be said that this is a practical necessity, since developing young need just such an abundance of neatly packaged, highly concentrated food as insects represent. But even granting that insect-eating at this stage is only a case of opportunism, the sequence of events is still a repetition of the evolutionary events that preceded it. It was the practical advantage afforded by the wealth of insect food that originally brought the reptile ancestors ashore; and so today the young of reptiles not only return to the feeding habits of their ancestors, but do so for the same ecological reasons. The young of the big tree iguana, who will later spend their days browsing and picking fruit off trees, begin by stalking and catching insects. The green sea turtle, almost completely herbivorous at maturity, starts by eating practically any kind of animal food.

A SIMILAR progression from insect diet to some specialized sort of feeding is to be seen in various kinds of snakes, which as a group are the most elaborately specialized feeders among the reptiles. Here, however, the change is not from animal food to a diet of plants, but rather from an infantile habit of insect-eating to whatever restricted food the adults may specialize in. The rat snakes of the genus *Elaphe*, for instance, when grown show strong preference for warm-blooded prey and for eggs, but very young rat snakes eat nearly any living thing that they can catch and swallow. During their earliest weeks of life this means insects; later on frogs are added to the list, and when finally an adequate body size is reached, the adult diet of mice, birds and eggs becomes practicable. In all these cases the progression of feeding habits is clearly dictated by the relative availability of food that the animal is able to take in.

It is their leglessness that most obviously sets the snakes apart from the lizards, their fellows in the order Squamata. Actually, however, feeding adaptations were also behind the initial evolutionary separation—and these are fully as striking as their lack of legs. The whole structure of a snake's head and jaws, for instance, is designed to provide the stretch that allows it to take in creatures bigger around than itself. This ability obviously gives snakes greater scope in their feeding outlook and, indeed, most adult snakes will either eat anything live that they can swallow or show some kind of curiously specialized food preference, like *Dasypeltis*, an African genus which eats only eggs. It might even be said that the gape of the snake made the snake plan feasible. In any case, of all the many ventures into limblessness which the Squamata have made, the only one that prospered markedly was the one that accompanied this extraordinary ability to accommodate oversized food.

Most lizards, on the other hand, have continued in the traditional insect-eating role. Though some among them will occasionally pick up small pieces of bread or bits of fruit thrown to them, eating pieces of objects rather than whole objects is really out of character for the Squamata.

In eating very small prey, lizards simply grab and swallow, but when they feed on larger animals they employ a swallowing technique called inertial feeding. Objects too big to be taken in forthwith are seized and then engulfed by a process involving a sudden relaxing of the jawhold, followed by a quick sideways thrust that moves the jaw a little farther over the object. The grip is again relaxed, the axis of the head is shifted the other way, and a new bite is made with the other side of the jaw forward. The inertia of the object gives the advancing jaws something to push against. That lizards carry out the process by moving first one side of the jaw forward and then the other forecasts the far more specialized "jaw-walking" method of swallowing carried out by snakes.

The feeding techniques of snakes is, as noted, one of their fundamentally distinctive features, and it involves some remarkable structural modifications of the head and jaws. Besides reductions in the facial skeleton which free the jaws from the brain case behind, the brain itself is encased in bone as a protection against contact with the oversized and often resisting food. The front ends of the lower jaw are not tightly joined at the chin, but only loosely connected by a ligament. Each of the lower jawbones is thus a freely movable unit. This gives the mouth a monstrous gape and stretch limited only by the elasticity of the soft tissues of the mouth and throat. To this arrangement are added recurved teeth and a complex set of muscles that operate in a way that allows each side of the jaw to be manipulated separately. The snake takes in its food by simply moving one side of the jaw forward to a toothhold, then walking the other side alternately a little farther still, then going back to the first side and moving it up again, and so on. The recurved teeth hold the prey firmly while the jaw is biting but disengage freely as each side is alternately pushed forward for a new grip.

It is not surprising that snakes have evolved a number of supplementary adaptations to help exploit their gape. To avoid interruption of its breathing, for example, a snake swallowing a big rat or frog extends its glottis beyond the end of the lower jaw and through it takes in air as a diver breathes through a snorkel tube. Another modification related to feeding is constriction, a maneuver by which the snake throws turns of its body around the prey and suffocates it by squeezing it. The coils of a constrictor are thrown on with incredible speed, and control in some cases is so good that a rat snake, for instance, can entwine and kill at least three baby rabbits at the same time, thus making the most of the opportunity offered by a rabbit nest.

To most people constricting seems one of the more lurid and unpardonable things that snakes do, and through the centuries the habit has evoked a great deal of morbid lore. For example, though I come from an enlightened family, I grew up thinking that a constricting snake snatches up its prey, throws on coils and with chiropractic precision pulverizes each separate bone in its victim's body, licks the pulped prey all over to lubricate it, zestfully engulfs it and then lays up somewhere for a year or more, stupefied by its excesses.

Only part of this is true. The speed with which the coils are applied is striking and the force they exert is great. There is rarely any crushing of bones, however, no laving with slime till the food is on the way down and in most cases little shaping and molding of the victim's contours for easy swallowing.

Although pythons and boas usually come to mind first when we think of constrictors, the constricting habit is more widespread among smaller snakes. Perhaps the most diminutive is the slender short-tailed snake of central Florida which overpowers other little snakes for eating by squeezing them into quiescence—just as its bigger relative the king snake also does. The same muscula-

HOW SNAKES SWALLOW LARGE OBJECTS

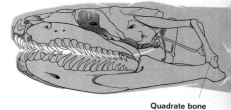

Quadrate bone

SNAKE JAW CLOSED

A versatile jaw enables snakes to swallow their food headfirst and whole, even when the victim is larger in diameter than the snake's body, and may even be alive and kicking. The quadrate bone, connecting the lower jaw loosely to the skull, works like a double-jointed hinge so that the snake can drop its lower jaw at the back of its mouth as well as at the front. The lower jaw can also be stretched sideways, since its two halves are connected at the chin by an elastic muscle. Sharp, recurved teeth hold the quarry in place while the snake, moving first one side and then the other of its mobile jaws, seems to "walk" its gaping mouth forward around its food.

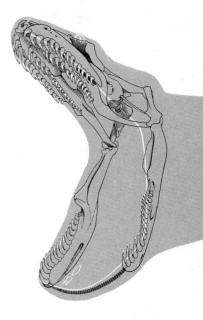

SNAKE JAW DISTENDED

ture that is used in constricting is also useful in climbing trees and most, though not all, constricting snakes are partly arboreal.

Just as remarkable as constriction, and even more refined as a device for taking big prey, is venom injection. Some of the consequences of this extraordinary feeding device will be discussed further on.

As a group, then, the snakes can be regarded as the most strongly modified reptiles in regard to food-taking adjustments. Theirs is a broad-scale specialization, however, involving the whole suborder to which they belong. Throughout the class Reptilia, curious side ventures in hunting or food-taking may be found in single genera or even species.

Turtles are on the whole the least elaborate feeders among reptiles, but they too have their specialized members. The classic examples are two unlovely creatures that live on the bottoms of streams and sloughs and take prey by ambush. One is the aforementioned South American matamata the other is the alligator snapper of the southeastern United States, which not only uses camouflage as the matamata does, but adds to this a fishing lure for decoying victims.

MECHANICS OF THE CHAMELEON'S TONGUE

For years it was thought that the tongue of the chameleon, which is hollow, was "blown" out of its mouth like the finger of a glove. Now it is understood that its firing is under the control of two sets of muscles. One set runs the length of the tongue and keeps it packed in tight pleats on a pointed bone in the back of the mouth like a spring coiled on a stick.

When the chameleon spots an insect it opens its mouth, moves the whole apparatus forward, and contracts a second set of muscles that circle the tongue like a series of tiny automobile tires. When contracted, they tend to squeeze the tongue forward off the central bone (top). The chameleon "fires" by suddenly relaxing the long muscles; the tongue shoots forward like a released spring (bottom), given added impetus by a squeezing action of ring muscles.

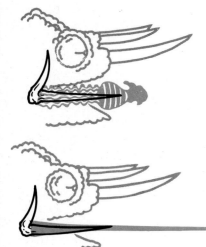

THE alligator snapper is a big, dun-colored turtle with a three-keeled shell, a huge lumpy head, strong jaws, and musculature that snaps the jaws forward and shut in a lightning-fast strike. Other turtles are able to strike as fast and powerfully, but the alligator snapper has something extra to draw prey within reach. In murky water it looks like a lump of mud or part of the bottom. Its shell and swollen head are generally scarred, eroded, and bearded with algae. Even its eyes are camouflaged by a broad turret of skin that protrudes from the margins of the orbit and partly surrounds the eye, which thus peers out from the depths of a little hole. The device is strikingly like that of the turreted eye of an African chameleon and evidently serves the same general function. The small area of iris visible is spread with black spots, each comparable to the pupil in size, and by the redundance of these the pupil itself is rendered meaningless to the observer. At least, that is the way it looks to a human observer and the alligator snapper certainly seems to use this equipment as useful camouflage in feeding. It spends a great deal of its time lying in the murk with its jaws wide open, sometimes still, sometimes with its head swaying slowly back and forth. Look inside its mouth, and if the light is good enough you will see what appears to be the two ends of an earthworm fastened in the middle by a short stalk from the floor of the mouth. The object looks like a worm, and it is quite clearly used as a lure to attract fishes into striking distance. It is under complete muscular control, and can be pointed in any direction and extended and contracted in ways strikingly similar to the contortions of an earthworm that finds itself in water. I have never seen a fish grab this bait, but others have. And many times I have seen an alligator turtle open its jaws wide the instant a fish came near, then move the "worm" about suggestively in a way that ought to appeal deeply to any fish not aware that this was actually part of a fish-eating turtle.

The matamata is the most thoroughly inanimate-looking of all turtles—perhaps of all vertebrate animals. Its weird appearance is not simply a misfortune, but rather a clearly utilitarian adjustment to a way of getting food. The matamata not only looks like a pile of debris, but its limbs and grotesquely flattened head are fringed and festooned with shreds and filaments of itself that should, and must, seem to a small fish like edible refuse. In any case, small fishes do come up and nibble and snatch at these projections, and are often quickly sucked in by a remarkable sort of hydraulic trap the matamata uses in place of the strike and jawhold of the snappers and soft-shelled turtles. The matamata's jawbones are weak and rubbery, serving as little more than a hooplike support for the front edge of the greatly distensible mouth and throat. As the head shoots forward at the prey the jaws open wide, the throat distends tremendously, sucking a quick flood of water into the mouth, and washing in anything in the neighborhood that is not strongly anchored.

Except for these and a few other cases of specialization for ambush, turtles are mostly straightforward, simple feeders and some of them, like the American box turtles, are the most nearly omnivorous of any reptiles.

Odd or narrowly specialized diets are more commonly found among snakes and lizards. There are, for instance, lizards that specialize in ants. The Asiatic gliding lizards of the genus *Draco* are among these and since *Draco* is arboreal, it finds its chief source of food among tree-dwelling species of ants. The horned lizards of the American West, and the marvelously spiny Australian moloch are other anteaters. It was pointed out earlier that no one knows why such a habit should be furthered by having the wild and spiky appearance that horned lizards and molochs have.

THE African egg-eating snakes of the genus *Dasypeltis* have become specifically modified for a diet of eggs. Various other kinds of snakes eat eggs, of course, but *Dasypeltis* is committed entirely to the exploitation of the habit. The eggs have to be eaten whole—a snake's tongue is too wispy to lap up their contents. For a handless creature to engulf a big, smooth, oval egg with a surface too hard for a toothhold seems next to impossible—a feat compared to which bobbing for apples is the merest child's play—and the accomplishments of *Dasypeltis* in this line are imposing. The distensibility of its mouth is perhaps greater than that of any other snake. The lining of the mouth, when not stretched around an egg, lies in folds and pleats. While most kinds of snakes, when they have swallowed an egg, either break it by contractions of the body wall or simply wait for the shell to dissolve, *Dasypeltis* has sharp projections from the neck vertebrae that rip the shell open as it goes down the gullet. There is a special set of muscles for regurgitating the shells, and a valve for keeping the liquid egg-contents down while the shells come up. What advantage *Dasypeltis* finds in specializing so narrowly is not clear. Perhaps it is just that being exclusively an eater of eggs allows one to be a very successful eater of eggs.

There is a whole subfamily of slender tree snakes, the Dipsadinae, that feeds mainly on slugs and snails. Both their tooth equipment and their psychology are specialized for overcoming the reluctance of a sticky snail to come out of a shell which would be a nuisance to swallow. There are turtles and lizards that eat snails too, but most of them crudely smash up the shells with flat jaw surfaces or blunt teeth, swallow fragments of them along with the occupant and are then faced with the job of defecating the broken pieces. As if to show the greater refinement of snakes in all dietary matters, *Dipsas* has developed a specially modified lower jaw, and plucks out the snail with elongated teeth.

The most parochial of all reptile victualers I have heard of is a little burrowing snake, without a common name, known technically as *Leptotyphlops
phenops*. It feeds on the contents of termites' abdomens which it apparently
sucks out of the skin, leaving it and the thorax behind. Besides being strangely
restricted, this diet is also the only one among snakes that involves the taking
of pieces of a food object rather than the whole thing. All the rest of the snakes
eat whole objects, with none of the chewing or tearing apart of food practiced
by crocodilians and by some turtles.

One of the most refined hunting devices among reptiles is the insect-trapping
tongue of the true chameleons. The tongue can be popped out for a distance
equal to about one and a half times the length of the body of the animal, not
including the tail. The end of the tongue is an enlarged bulb covered with an
adhesive that will hold good-sized active prey—mostly insects, but sometimes
even small birds and reptiles. A toad, of course, also uses a sticky tongue as an
insect trap, but the way the chameleon shoots its tongue forward is very different. The tongue of the chameleon is hollow, and when not in use is bunched
up, accordionlike, on a smooth, tapered cartilaginous projection of the bony
throat structure, or hyoid apparatus. As the chameleon approaches a victim—
which it does with diabolical stealth—the whole tongue assembly shifts to a
ready station toward the front of the mouth. The force that shoots the tongue
out when it is triggered is a spasmic contraction of a ring of muscle built into
the structure of the forward section of the tongue. This squeezes down on the
lubricated taper of the spike of cartilage like two fingers squeezing down on a
watermelon seed, except that in this case it is the squeezing tongue that shoots
out. At the same instant opposing muscles let go, and the tongue runs forward
so fast that it flies out full length before it is finally stopped by elastic fibers
in its wall. It is withdrawn by contractions of longitudinal muscles.

THE chameleon is as fully committed to living in trees as any reptile in the
world and its tongue is a trap for small tree-dwelling creatures. The tongue
trap would not work very well on the ground. There are generally too many
obstructions close to the ground for such long-range shooting; moreover, the
tongue sags at the end of the trajectory and its sticky surface would pick up
dirt. In any case, chameleons are arboreal and their whole architecture is adjusted to living in trees. Their twig-grasping feet look like the jaws of pliers.
Their eyes roll about freely, wholly independent of one another, hidden in the
depths of ported turrets that shield their glint except from the ill-fated creature on which they focus, and for whom the glint would generally come too late.

The famous chameleon color-changes range through a variety of hues and
shifts of pattern. Most chameleons are able to assume colors and patterns that
blend into their surroundings. The dwarf chameleons of the genus *Brookesia*
have more or less fixed patterns and a body form that in silhouette suggests a
leaf. In southern Nyasaland I once came upon three of these fat little lizards in
deep rain forest on the southern slopes of Mount Mlanje, all unaccountably on
the ground and all plodding the same way across the dim trail I was following.
I have no idea what they were doing down there out of the trees, but they seemed
to have in mind some place to go; and seeing three of them within a hundred
yards, tottering ahead on their pincer feet, was like witnessing a ritual migration of some mysterious kind. Though the migratory band was only three, it was
quite an event for me because the Mlanje dwarf chameleon is a scarce animal.

Adaptations are neither acquired nor used in a vacuum. From the start, and increasingly as they are perfected, new structures and functions are bound to affect and be affected by the whole organization of the animal. A modification occurs, and there follows a whole system of other changes to compensate for it or to exploit it. The idea is beautifully shown in some of the ramifications of venom production in reptiles, which is clearly related to the basic snake specialty of going after oversized food too active to be merely seized and swallowed.

Of all the feeding adaptations of reptiles, the ability of certain snakes and of the lizards, the Gila monster and its close relative the Mexican beaded lizard, to kill prey by the injection of poison seems the most dramatic. The poison of snakes fascinated men long before Cleopatra clutched the famous asp to her bosom, and it has probably inspired as much myth and folklore as any adaptation in the animal kingdom. Humans, of course, experience it primarily as a defensive weapon used by the snakes, since man is not a part of any poisonous reptile's food plan; but man has a way of making these things his own, forgetting the main and original purpose which such adaptations serve—in this case, the procuring of food. Thus the lore and legend of snake venom usually revolves around human experience, and the rabbit or rat or other small mammal that is the normal victim of a poison snake dies and is eaten in obscurity.

R EPTILE poison is modified saliva. All snakes have well-developed salivary glands, the secretions of which help to lubricate the big objects that their wide gape allows them to swallow. In the venomous snakes, certain of these salivary glands have been converted into poison producers. In the poisonous colubrids, for instance, a gland just under the lip scales sends venom into grooved, fixed teeth in the rear of the upper jaw. In the vipers it is another gland, located below and behind the eye, that produces the poison and pipes it forward through a slender duct to the base of the fang.

Snake venom is made up of a variety of active substances, mostly proteins and enzymes. Some of these act principally on the circulatory system, clotting blood cells and destroying capillary walls. Such poisons are called hemotoxic or hemorrhagic. Other snake venoms are neurotoxic, acting mainly on the nervous system, paralyzing muscles of the heart or breathing apparatus or both. Although there is a great deal of individual and specific variation in the make-up and strength of venoms, the vipers in general have poisons of the former type, killing by circulatory disruptions, heavy bleeding, and destruction of tissues, while the venom of cobralike snakes in general paralyzes the prey.

The needles for the hypodermic injection or introduction of venom are, of course, modified teeth. In Gila monsters they are several grooved teeth in both the upper and lower jaws. Poison seeps into the grooves from furrows in the lining of the mouth which lead from multiple gland-openings, a rather inefficient arrangement that makes it impossible for these lizards to use the swift stab of the poisonous snakes—instead they must bite and hang on. Fangs of the cobra group retain traces of a groove on the fore margins, showing that they formed by infolding along the anterior surface. Some cobras are able to spit their poison. The herpetologist Charles Bogert made a careful study of cobra fangs and found that their unsettling ability to throw a fine stream of poison several feet ahead can be explained by the arrangement of the opening at the fang tip. This is so placed that venom under pressure from behind comes out at right angles to the long axis of the tooth. Among most poisonous snakes the venom holes are at the tips of fangs. For such a snake to squirt venom forward and upward at a useful angle to hit something in front of it, it would have to

HOW A RATTLESNAKE RELEASES VENOM

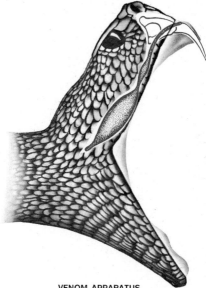

VENOM APPARATUS

When a rattlesnake opens its mouth to strike, its long fangs, which have lain folded flat along the roof of its mouth, are swung into the position shown in the drawing above, and can be plunged into the victim's flesh with one swift jab of the snake's head. As the fangs sink in, muscles contract and squeeze a venom gland in each cheek, forcing the poison out through a narrow tube that runs from gland to fang.

FANG OF RATTLER

A cross section of a rattler's fang reveals the hollow tube that carries venom (shown in color) from the venom sac to a hole near the tooth's tip. This is the most efficient way for snakes to conduct poison. In others the poison trickles along an open canal or even a simple groove in the fang and may spill out. But by conserving its venom in a closed pipeline, the rattlesnake can fell its victim with a single bite.

59

WARNING DEVICES

THE INDIAN COBRA

Confronted by danger, the cobra flattens the skin of its neck into a wide hood, which makes it look bigger than it is. It does this by spreading long, movable ribs.

THE RATTLESNAKE

To warn away enemies, the rattlesnake shakes the hollow segments that form the rattle at the end of its tail. Each time it sheds its skin, it adds one new section.

THE CORAL SNAKE

The red, yellow and black bands of the venomous coral snake act as a warning flag to other animals. Some harmless species imitate its stripes to bluff their enemies.

have an unreasonably wide gape even for a snake, and in addition would have to tilt its head far back over its body. In the case of a spitting cobra, because the hole at the fang tip faces forward, it is able to discharge its poison with the mouth only slightly agape. There is some question as to the utility of the spitting adaptation. Although it blinds victims temporarily, or even permanently, it cannot be thought of as an effective way of immobilizing prey, and thus must be an adaptation for discouraging potential enemies.

In vipers the fang canal is completely and smoothly enclosed. Viper fangs are very long, and to keep them from piercing the floor of the mouth they fold back against its roof by a rolling movement of the shortened maxillary bone on which they are mounted. One or more pairs of spare fangs are usually arranged in formation behind the pair being used. Because the duct from the poison gland fits over the base of the spare teeth as well as over that of the fang in use, the loss of a fang does not hold up matters at all—the spare comes forward, alongside the functional fang, and is ready for use.

To show how the consequences of an adaptation like poison are spread through the whole make-up of an animal, it is interesting to examine the rattlesnake. Like most snakes, rattlesnakes take live prey, and their poison enables them to take relatively large animals with a minimum of effort and risk. Being snakes, they also show the drastic remodeling of the head that lets them swallow big food—which has the dual advantage of increasing the number of different kinds of things they can eat and enabling them to go longer on one meal, if that meal is a big one.

All of this depends, of course, on the rattler's being able to find, immobilize and, without being injured in the process, swallow the prey and then digest it properly—and all of its equipment is geared to do just that. To detect the nearness of warm-blooded prey, even in the dark, rattlesnakes (and all of the pit vipers) have the heat-feeling pits characteristic of their kind. These are cavities a little larger than the nostril, located on either side of the snout between the nostril and the eye. They are sculptured out of the maxillary bone and are lined with sensory cells specially designed to detect changes in radiant heat. They evidently are the counterparts of less elaborate pits in the lip scales of boas and pythons which have been shown to function in a similar way. These pits tell the rattlesnake of the presence of warm-blooded animals as far as a foot and a half away, and help guide the range and direction of the strike.

Once the victim has been stabbed, the poison immediately comes into play, and since it contains a spreading agent to speed its distribution, its effects are sure. The victim rarely drops dead in its tracks (although I once saw a fox terrier fall three yards from where it had been bitten by a six-and-a-half-foot diamondback rattler), but usually runs off in a panic and falls some distance away. For this reason the rattlesnake's specialized feeding equipment should be designed to cope with this situation too—and it is, in the form of the adaptation known as Jacobson's organ.

This organ comprises a pair of cavities located internally on each side of the snout with ducts leading to an opening in the roof of the mouth. The cavities are heavily supplied with nerve endings like those used in the smell sense. The tongue picks up odorous particles from the ground or out of the air itself and transfers them to the openings of Jacobson's organ, thus enabling the rattlesnake to trail its victim. Although the process seems to overlap the regular olfactory sense, it does not replace it. Many reptiles with well-developed Jacobson's organs are able to smell in the ordinary way too. This curious organ is not used in food-getting alone, but seems to be put to important social uses such as the forming of hibernating groups and the finding of one sex by another at mating time. Nevertheless, its part in the complex of feeding adaptations of the rattlesnake is evident. It is the only link that the poisonous snake has with the poisoned, doomed but still mobile prey.

Once the rattlesnake has caught up with its now dead or dying victim, it brings to bear the snake-wide ability to fit its jaws over huge packages of food. A four-foot rattler can swallow a full-grown cottontail rabbit. Moreover, it is able to provide itself with cottontails to swallow, something a nonvenomous snake could only rarely do. Nor does the interaction of adaptations end there. Because snake venom contains digestive enzymes, the process of digestion begins as soon as the venom diffuses into the tissues of the prey. This, too, is important in terms of economy of effort. Nonpoisonous snakes, especially the constrictors, which subdue big prey by squeezing them into immobility, must digest without the help of any internal enzyme action in their food. But for the rattlesnake, digestion of the huge bulk proceeds from the inside as well as at the surface, and there is little doubt that the time involved is greatly shortened —with whatever attendant profit the saving of time might yield to the snake.

The usefulness of venom is not confined to feeding alone. Its potential advantages as a defense mechanism are obviously also powerful. However, this point is not so simple as it might seem at first glance. For while it is clear that poison is a good thing to stay away from, how will another animal know that a snake is poisonous? The question leads to some interesting conclusions.

In feeding activity, of course, there is no conceivable reason why a snake should warn its prey of its venomous intentions. To convert feeding mechanisms to defense, however, either against attack by snake-eating predators or against the hazard of being accidentally trod upon by heavy animals of any sort, some means of advertisement—a warning system—that will prevent the attack would seem to be required. Violent encounters in nature are generally disadvantageous, even to a poisonous snake, and any device that will reduce their frequency is bound to be a good thing to have. It is evidently for this very reason that coral snakes are usually brilliantly colored and marked, that cobras rise high and spread spectacular hoods, and that the rattlesnake sounds its rattle.

IT may never be possible to prove satisfactorily that a rattlesnake evolved its rattle as a safety device, but common sense certainly supports this conclusion. Such mechanisms, however, if they actually work as they seem to, work in a complicated way. They must depend for their effect on a reactive mechanism in the potential enemy—that is to say, a concurrent evolutionary change that might produce in deer, for example, a tendency to shun fancily banded snakes or in coyotes to jump away from the buzz of a rattlesnake's rattle. This is not hard to imagine, however. There are abundant cases in nature in which two different kinds of animals go through concomitant evolutionary changes that fit them for beneficial contacts with each other or reduce friction between them. In the relationships among living things harmony is at least as important as strife as a means of survival. A crab may cause havoc among the small animals that are its food, but at the same time it tolerantly goes about with a sea anemone on its back, or even makes overt moves to put the anemone there. The stinging cells of the anemone are protection for the crab, and the scraps from the crab's feeding are eaten by its partner.

Though at first glance it may seem silly to use such an example to illustrate the relationship between poisonous snakes and other animals, it is not silly at all. Both the rattlesnake and a bison, say, are potentially dangerous to each other. Neither can get the slightest good out of contact with the other. On the other hand, both can profit immensely by staying cleanly out of one another's way. What, then, is more logical than that the snake should evolve a warning device, and the potential enemy—the inadvertent trampler—the psychology to react to the warning? Even a carnivore that usually ate snakes—unless it was immune to snake venom—would logically be better off if it had a heritable ability to recognize, or to *learn* to recognize, harmful snakes. Then it could go about its business of eating harmless snakes without any trouble. The candy-stick coloration of coral snakes would surely entrench any such discriminatory capacity as might be found naturally in a coon or a hawk or any other snake-eating predator. So would the rattlesnake's hair-raising song.

THE idea of a poisonous animal evolving a warning device that will work only if a potential enemy also evolves the sense to react to the warning is hard for some people to accept. I do not know why this should be so. Besides logic, a great store of anecdotal evidence supports its reality. Nearly any mature Florida bird dog, for instance, reacts instantly to the sound of a rattlesnake. While it is hard to be sure what a dog has learned from previous experience or from other dogs, it can in most of the cases I know about be confidently said that the learning process did not involve being bitten by a rattlesnake. A pointer I used to hunt with in central Florida, though it had never been bitten by a poisonous snake in its life, showed unmistakable evidence of associating the rattle with a particularly odious situation. In its quartering for quail, if you saw it suddenly jump into the air and you went to the spot to see what had scared it, one of two things was most often there—a coiled diamondback, or a bush of a certain species of *Crotalaria*, the dry pods of which rattle when disturbed, almost like a rattler's alarm. Only one of the several species of *Crotalaria* sounds authentically like a snake, and only that species used to make my dog jump. But the effect of a collision with that was electric, and for all the years of its life the dog rose like a bird when it stirred the fearful noise from a diamondback or from the bush that I think sounded the same to the dog.

That is of course not a scientific observation. It involves a subjective judgment on my part, and the behavior of only one dog. And it in any case leaves unanswered the question whether the reaction is innate in canines or is learned by associating the sound of the rattle with the bites or aggressive behavior of snakes in general—or is learned from other dogs. That dogs are of Old World —and rattlesnakes of American—origin makes it unlikely that the pointer was born genetically able to associate the sound with the snake. On the other hand, the buzzing of rattlesnakes is really just an elaboration of a tendency of many kinds of snakes to vibrate the tail when approached by a potential enemy. The vibration is often soundless, but in dry leaves it makes a little rattling or humming noise. Possibly dog ancestors evolved the capacity to associate such a sound with ill-tempered or dangerous snakes. But the important point is that the rattle of the rattlesnakes makes little sense unless it can be thought of as an agent of advantage to the bearer. And the advantage in not being stepped on by a bison or chopped up by the teeth of a wolf seems pretty clear. That the bison and wolf might go away poisoned and die would be little comfort to the snake. Its profit would come from preventing the encounter from happening.

A CALIFORNIA KING SNAKE LUNGES AT A WARY KANGAROO RAT. ITS DIET CONSISTS OF MANY RODENTS AND SNAKES, INCLUDING RATTLERS

The Snake as Hunter

Of all reptiles, snakes are the most highly specialized hunters and feeders. Be they small as worms or bigger than the king snake above, they all subdue and swallow live prey, eating meat exclusively with an economy of risk and effort which few animals of any kind can match. The portfolio of photographs on the following pages records their vigor as trenchermen, their skill as hunters.

63

SQUEEZING STEADILY, a pine snake kills a white rat. Constrictors do not crush their victims, as many people have long thought; their coils make it harder and harder for the prey to breathe until it finally suffocates.

WITH A GOOD GRIP on the head of an anole lizard, this vine snake will settle itself and slowly swallow it. Vine snakes are long and slender; they lurk in foliage and pounce on lizards creeping among the leaves.

The Devices of Snakes for Subduing Food

Though limbless, lethargic and small-brained, the snake is one of the most perfectly efficient predators in the animal world. Elastic jaw joints let it accommodate any prey of reasonable size. A slim body lets it prowl or lie in ambush inconspicuously. A slow metabolism enables it to wait weeks for the right meal. If food walks by that might put up a dangerous fight, a snake can usually afford to ignore it.

Once a snake does attack, its problem is to find an end where it can start swallowing. If its victim is slender, like the lizard opposite, the snake can simply throw its open mouth directly over the creature's head. But if the victim is wriggly and fat, like the rat above, the snake has to immobilize it first, by wrapping coils around it boa-fashion, or—if the snake is poisonous—by giving it a quieting shot of venom.

65

A Super Swallower

A sure way around the problem of subduing live flesh is to catch it young enough. The two-foot African snake *Dasypeltis scaber*, shown here, has carried this solution to the ultimate point of eating nothing but birds' eggs, and has become marvelously specialized for this task. Its teeth have dwindled to nubbins which are useful only for gripping a smooth egg. Its jaws are loosely connected to its skull by two swiveling bones which can be dropped down to give *Dasypeltis* the most stretchy mouth of any snake. In its throat are sharp projections sticking down from the backbone and used to rip open eggshells.

AN APPARENTLY IMPOSSIBLE TASK confronts the African egg-eater as it opens its mouth to swallow a mountainous-looking egg with a diameter well over twice the width of its own body.

WITH JAWS AT MAXIMUM GAPE, the snake manages to get its mouth around the egg. The pleated lining inside the mouth and the flexible tissues between the jawbones are stretched as far as they will go. The tiny, backward-pointing teeth work their way across the egg's huge smooth dome, and the fountains of the snake's saliva flow freely so that the egg will slide in smoothly.

A valve at the entrance of its stomach will take yolks and whites but will reject pieces of shell. These are regurgitated by special throat muscles that bundle them together, sharp edges in, so that they do not scratch on the way up.

One trouble with an egg diet is that birds lay only in season, and a snake may have to go for a long time without food. Its ability to regurgitate shells is a help here. First, no space inside the snake is wasted on useless materials—if it comes on several eggs it can eat them all. Second, no energy is burned up in passing the shells through the digestive system.

UP COME THE SHELL FRAGMENTS, still attached to their underlying membrane, their jagged edges wadded in together. All the nourishing egg fluids have been drained and swallowed.

COMPLETELY INSIDE the snake's mouth, the egg begins to pass down its elastic throat, where it will come in contact with the sharp internal spines which will break it open. Being roughly spherical, an egg is remarkably resistant to crushing, but once pierced by the spines it will break into small fragments very quickly as it is subjected to muscle spasms of the snake's neck.

67

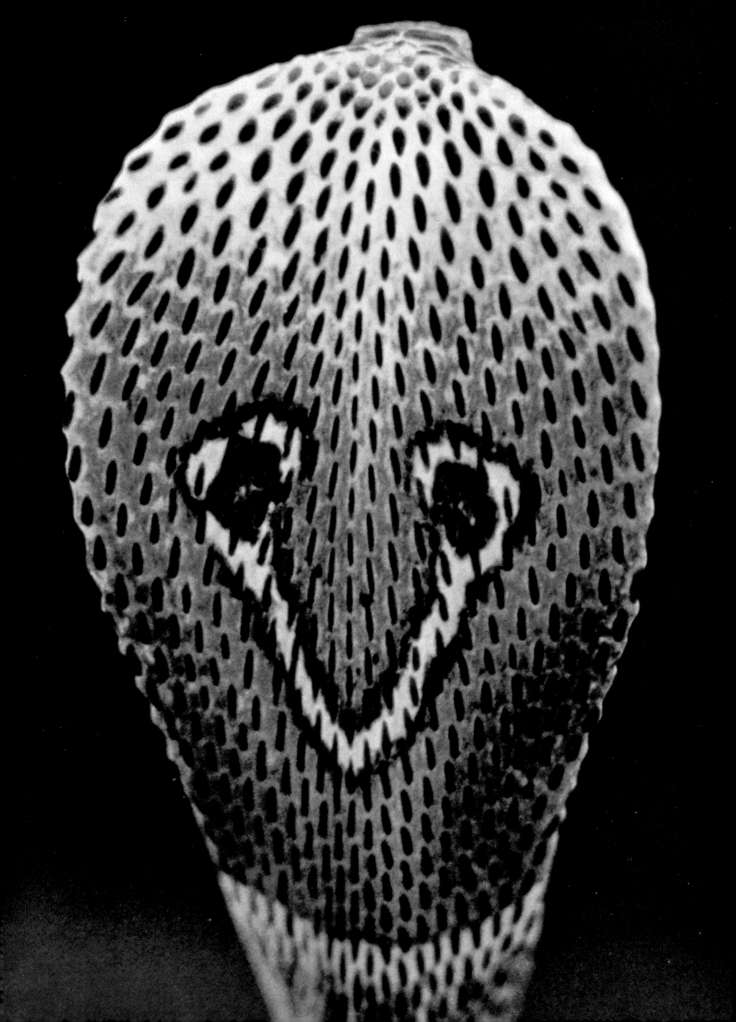

The Infamous Cobra

Although several other species are more deadly, the cobra has the worst reputation of any venomous snake. This is partly because of its large size and fearsome appearance, but mainly because it comes in constant contact with people in crowded Asiatic countries where few have shoes. As a result, it takes about 10,000 lives a year in India alone.

There are 12 species of cobras in the world, spreading from Africa east through southern Asia to the Philippines. Like their close relatives the mambas, the coral snakes and the kraits, they manufacture a mainly neurotoxic venom and eject it through fixed fangs in the front of the upper jaws. These are shorter than the fangs of vipers, and to use them effectively the cobra must resort to grasping and chewing to produce a series of wounds, rather than a single deep stab like a rattler's. Cobras have their own way of advertising their deadliness; they hiss loudly, rear up to a third of their length and spread their necks in the menacing "hood" shown in these pictures.

THE KING COBRA, rare but lethal, sometimes grows to 18 feet. It builds a nest of leaves which it watches until the young hatch, and is regarded by some as the world's most intelligent snake.

THE FEARSOME FACE of a spectacled cobra is actually no face at all but a set of black and white markings on the back of the cobra's neck which it spreads defensively when it is disturbed.

A BABY INDIAN COBRA is ready for business and its venom is as deadly as its parents' from the instant it hatches from its egg. The incubation period for this species is about two months.

69

SPITTING VENOM, an African black-necked cobra can squirt droplets of liquid with considerable accuracy for distances of up to eight feet. This is the same stuff that would kill a victim if injected into the blood stream. It is not injurious to the skin, but if it gets in the eyes it produces a burning sensation, and if it is not washed out immediately it can seriously damage the eyes

and in some cases even produce blindness. Three species of cobra have the ability to spit, and in all of them it is made possible by the location of the venom hole on the front of the fang, so that when a jet is shot out by the snake it goes forward and upward. There is some evidence that spitting cobras make an instinctive effort to aim directly at the eyes of their enemies.

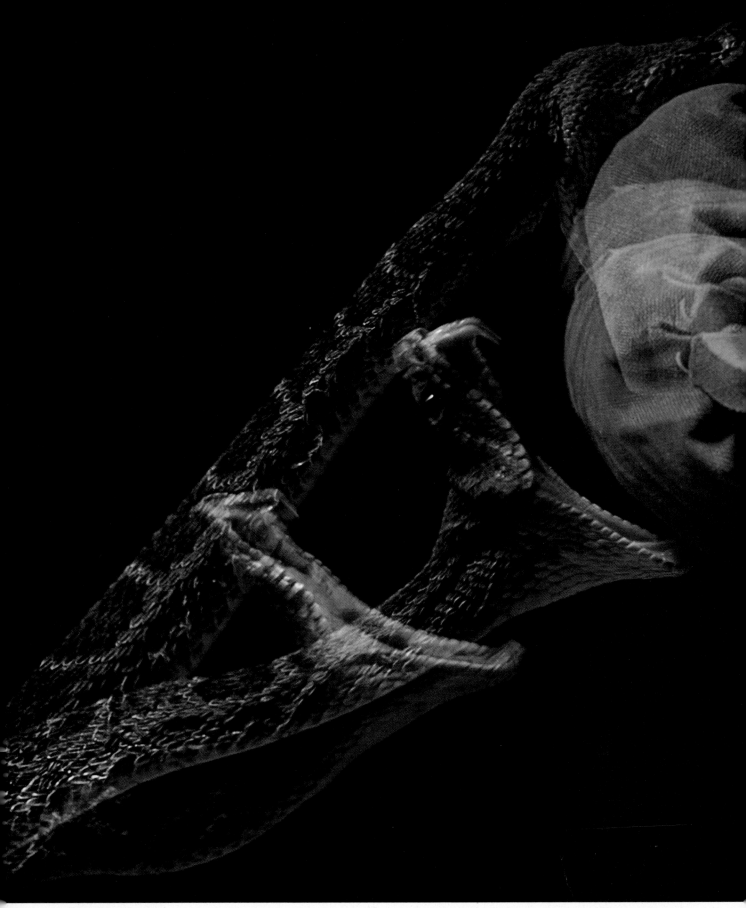

THE GAPING STRIKE of a rattler is revealed stroboscopically at three successive instants as the rattler lunges to sink its fangs into a warm piece of cotton batting. This sequence of laboratory photographs shows that the rattler—though a stabbing viper—can also bite in the ordinary way, with its lower venomless jaws making contact before the fangs administer the *coup de grâce*.

Fast Fangs of the Rattlers

Experts are constantly being asked: "Are cobras or rattlers the most poisonous?" Traditionally the prize has gone to the cobras, because if white rats are injected with equal amounts of cobra and rattler venom the cobra-injected animal will be the first to die. The true answer, however, is that both are deadly; the choice really depends on whether one prefers to die by paralysis (cobras) or by having one's tissues destroyed (rattlers). But the rattlesnake has it all over the cobra in the efficiency with which it delivers its venom. Its long poison fangs are located far forward in its jaws and are capable of a deep venom-filled stab at the first strike.

THE BLINDFOLD BITE of a rattler with taped eyes aims unerringly at the warm light bulb in a laboratory experiment, guided to the heat through nerves in two special sensory pits in its face.

THE STRAIGHT-ON STAB of a rattler is revealed in a light flash triggered by the pop of a balloon bursting under the rattler's jaws. Survival after such a bite depends on the size of the victim and on how much venom gets into the wound, which in turn depends on the size of the snake. The largest doses come from U.S. diamondbacks which can kill a 200-pound man in an hour.

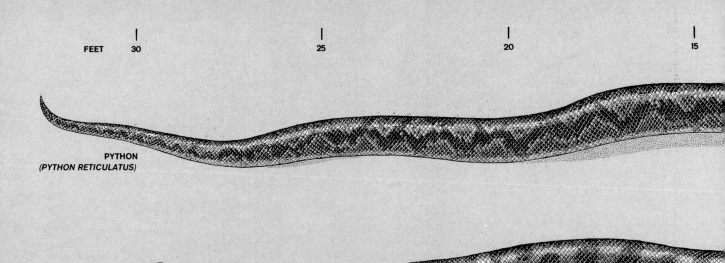

PYTHON
(PYTHON RETICULATUS)

ANACONDA
(EUNECTES MURINUS)

BOA
(CONSTRICTOR CONSTRICTOR)

COBRA
(OPHIOPHAGUS HANNAH)

The Sizes of Some Representative Snakes

Although jungle literature is full of accounts of immense snakes that can swallow animals as big as horses, and although fossil snakes of 50 feet have been uncovered, the largest snake in the world today is almost certainly under 40 feet. There are reliable reports of 37-foot South American swamp and river anacondas, but the largest snake ever accurately measured by a scientist was a 33-foot Asian reticulate python. Thus it receives top billing in this chart of representative snakes, arranged in order of maximum recorded length and with the largest animals they are known to eat.

The three biggest snake species are all constrictors. Contrary to belief, they do not break a victim's bones and squeeze it to a pulp, but they can and do loop a deer or a goat in several coils in a couple of seconds and squeeze until it suffocates. Large specimens in zoos have put down more than 100 pounds of meat in a single meal, and after such a feast a python is capable of going for a year or longer, if nothing else comes along, before eating again. It can and has eaten humans, but they are too often armed or in company with other humans and go too seldom into the python's haunts to be a significant item in its diet. Much more dangerous to men are the large poisonous snakes, notably the king cobra, a record specimen of which measures 18 feet 4 inches. Bushmasters of 12 feet and rattlers of eight feet have been caught. DeKay's snake averages a foot in length and can be found in New York's Central Park. But it is not the smallest species. Certain blind snakes are only five inches long when mature.

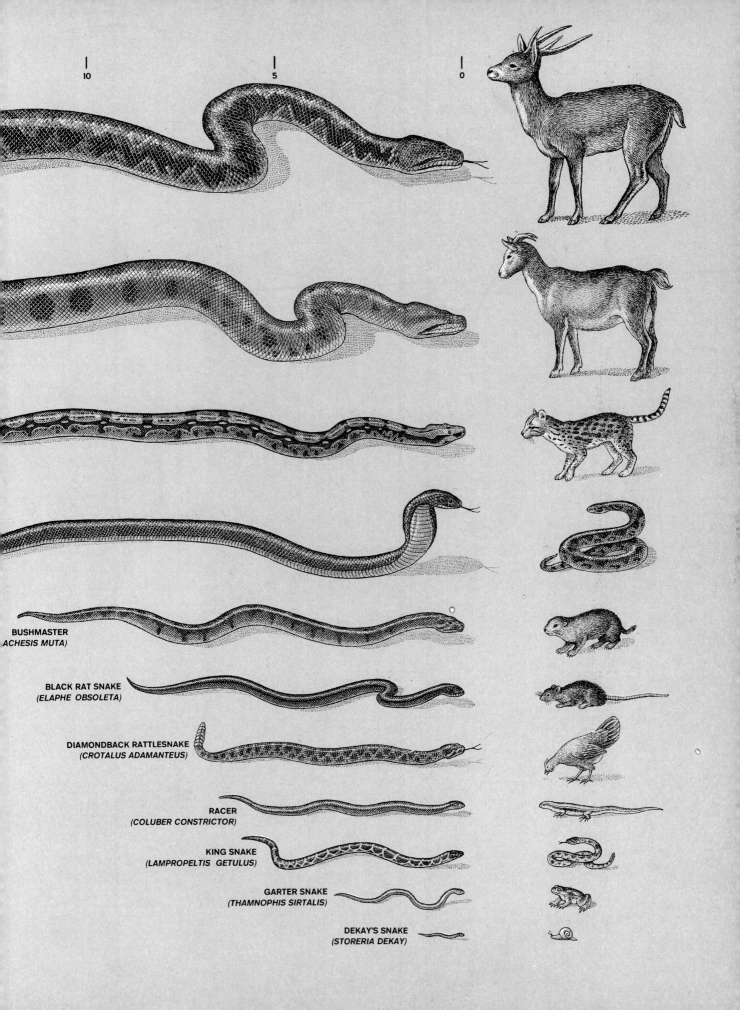

10   5   0

BUSHMASTER
(ACHESIS MUTA)

BLACK RAT SNAKE
(ELAPHE OBSOLETA)

DIAMONDBACK RATTLESNAKE
(CROTALUS ADAMANTEUS)

RACER
(COLUBER CONSTRICTOR)

KING SNAKE
(LAMPROPELTIS GETULUS)

GARTER SNAKE
(THAMNOPHIS SIRTALIS)

DEKAY'S SNAKE
(STORERIA DEKAY)

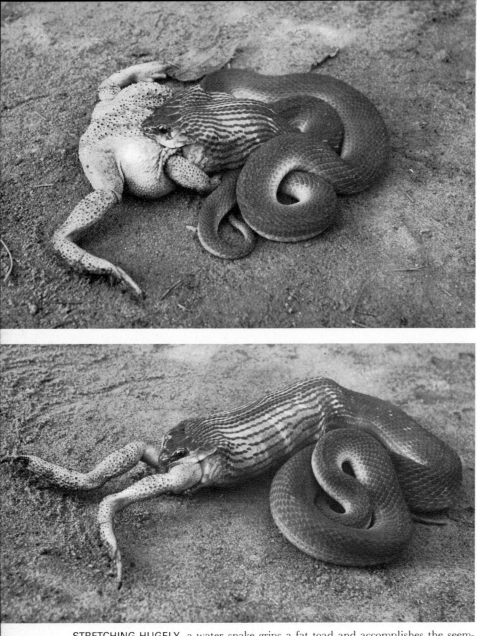

STRETCHING HUGELY, a water snake grips a fat toad and accomplishes the seemingly impossible task of swallowing it. In such everyday feats small common snakes duplicate in miniature the prodigious predations of pythons, boas or anacondas.

Tiny Terrors in the Grass

When man thinks of predators in the reptile world, he is likely to think of the large, dramatic animals like alligators, crocodiles, boas and rattlesnakes—creatures with whom his contacts are relatively rare. But to the small animals of field, forest and stream, it is the little garter snake or water snake that is the enemy, lying in wait in any clump of grass or marshy shoreline. The results of such an encounter are shown here—a swift and merciless struggle, and then the slow process of digestion, one life dissolved so that another may survive.

AN X-RAYED GARTER SNAKE discloses the long journey of a small animal through the snake's sinuous gut. The bulge at left is the carcass of a frog 84 hours after swallowing. The frog's hind limbs are already gone and its spine is beginning to dissolve.

4

The Business
of Living

REPTILES are found almost throughout the world. This does not mean that any reptile is likely to turn up in just any old place, or that any particular kind of reptile lives everywhere. It does mean that almost every part of the world is inhabited by reptiles of one kind or another and has something to offer them that they have made use of, be it in the water, the air, on the land or even under the land. Whether you are swimming or walking or climbing trees or digging in the ground, you are liable to encounter some sort of reptile, and you come upon them in every major region of the globe except Antarctica.

More than anywhere else, reptiles prosper and abound in the tropics. That is where most of the reptile families are represented. Some of these tropical families have representatives in the Temperate Zones too, but only two families are peculiar to the cooler regions of earth—a minor group of legless lizards in California and the tuatara on its chill New Zealand islands. Reptiles are not very good at withstanding cold. Only three species reach the Arctic. They seem to be even less able to put up with conditions at high altitudes, and there are almost none of them in the highest mountain zones.

The distribution of a plant or an animal through the world is known as its

TOO MUCH ALIKE
TO LIVE TOGETHER

Two lizard families, very similar in their adaptations and closely related, now have separate distributions in the two hemispheres. Iguanids, the older family, are almost entirely restricted to the New World, as shown by the areas of solid color on the top globe. Their counterparts, the agamids, live only in the Old World (lighter areas on bottom globe). It is tempting to speculate that the two families developed independently in their respective hemispheres, except for the fact that a few iguanids linger in isolated parts of the Old World: on Madagascar, and the Fiji and Tonga Islands in the western Pacific. Fossils in England and France have also been tentatively identified as iguanids of some 58 million years ago. Therefore it seems likely that this family was once worldwide, and persists today only where the later agamids have not been able to spread.

range. Range means simply geographic territory occupied. The ranges of reptiles, like those of any creature, are molded by several kinds of factors. Some of these are historical, reflecting the age of the species or group and the geologic events that have occurred in the region occupied. Others are ecological, involving the tolerances and preferences of the creature in question. A close look at the ranges of a number of reptiles—or of animals or plants of any kind—soon reveals that none of them, neither the young new species nor the old complex groups, appear to be occupying all the territory they should be capable of inhabiting. The reasons for this are diverse. Some are obscure, some clearly evident; all are worth thinking about.

Although complicated influences shape the ranges of animals, the fundamental fact is that patterns of distribution have been built, over a period of time, by animals spreading into suitable and accessible territory. Thus, other things being equal, the older a form of life is, the bigger its range will be. But other things are hardly ever equal, and while this principle is a necessary one to know, the conditions under which it alone applies are almost never found. Extraneous factors nearly always complicate the simple fundamental relation between time and spread.

For example, take the legless, blind lizard mentioned in Chapter 1 which I occasionally find when plowing on my farm. This worm lizard of the family Amphisbaenidae is found only in peninsular Florida. In the same region there is a scaly-backed swift, or fence, lizard, the Florida scrub lizard, which is also found nowhere else. These two lizards lead very different lives, but they occupy roughly the same territory—or, to put it differently, their habitats are very different but they have comparable geographic ranges. If the simple relation between time and spread were always applicable, it would follow that these two lizards have about the same background of history and age. Instead, however, they almost certainly originated many millions of years apart. The worm lizard belongs to a shrunken and ancient group with a drastically broken-up distribution which can be traced through a widespread fossil record, but it has today no near relative in Florida or even in continental North America. The scrub lizard, on the other hand, is closely related to other lizards in nearby areas, and may have diverged from them only a few million years ago, perhaps even in the same general area it now occupies.

Is the scrub lizard, then, spreading into new territory? It is not possible to say. In the case of the worm lizard, fossils show that the range of the group to which it belongs has contracted. But whether the Florida species is extending its territory or losing ground is anybody's guess.

Thinking of these two ranges as simple products of time and the ability of the animal to get about would bring one to mistaken conclusions. In any area, accounting for the distribution of each species found there is a demanding problem, and one that requires a careful appraisal of various evolutionary, ecological and paleogeographic events and processes. For every race that survives, many become extinct. Extinction eliminates not just single species, but whole clusters of lines—genera, families, and even orders. Thus the range of an old group nearly always will have been affected by the destructive process of extinction, as well as by the constructive one of spreading.

But in spite of the oddities of their distribution, reptiles are products of evolution—each kind originated in one place only—and for that reason their ranges over the earth do show certain regularities that allow generalizations to be made. One sort of generalization concerns the concentration of certain genera, families or orders of reptiles in particular geographic areas. On the separate continents the different reptile groups are represented in different ways. The spread of the crocodilians is very different from the complicated pattern turtles show. Lizards are distributed in yet another way, and not at all like the snakes, among which boids and colubrids have widely divergent geographic patterns. In most of these cases it is not possible to reconstruct the history—the origin and wanderings—of the group by simply studying its distribution. One of the few cases in which a major group of reptiles can be seen to have spread from a definite and recognizable center of origin is that of the advanced colubrid snakes. Their distribution strongly suggests that the Asiatic tropics are their ancestral land.

Another sort of regularity that a survey of the ranges of reptile groups reveals is a tendency for their distribution to correspond, in a general and average kind of way, with that of other plants and animals whose own ranges are more or less different. This is not a matter of exact correspondence of range limits, but rather a broad, global tendency for certain zones to share certain groups of animals and plants which are held there largely by climatic factors, while other types are excluded. Averaging out these correspondences in distribution provides the zoogeographer, whose task it is to study the relation of life to geographical areas, with a set of life regions that makes up a crude but sometimes useful pattern of world distribution of living things. The pattern, to be sure, is too broad to tell much about the individual species which occupy the life regions, but it does tell a good deal about the world as a place for life.

Animals wander and drift and are blown about the globe. Susceptibility to geographic dispersal of any kind has been given a special name: vagility. Any spreading that results in an extension of range is an expression of a creature's vagility. The capacity may or may not have to do with powers of locomotion. Marine animals, birds and stronger-flying insects tend to have bigger ranges than terrestrial species. On the other hand, some of the most delicate insects are distributed worldwide, evidently because they can so readily be transported by currents of air. Some of the most widespread of all animals are feeble creatures such as protozoa or crustacea, which have scarcely any locomotor ability at all, but whose cysts or eggs can be swirled about the world like dust, or carried from place to place in mud stuck on the feet of birds.

IN the study of the geographical distribution of animals, the inhabitants of islands are of special interest. The kinds of animals that live on an island are a clue to its past, to its possible connections with land areas in past geologic times. The record of sedimentary rocks is often hidden under water or under other deposits. Geologists, doubtful about the character and scheduling of connections among islands, turn to the distribution of plants, and especially of animals, for guidance. The evidence provided is indirect and often ambiguous or muddled, but it is frequently the best available.

To get trustworthy data from island animals, one has to be able to recognize cases of introduction by man. Geckos, for instance, are inveterate stowaways, and some of them have worked their way all over the tropics by just being on hand when man's cargoes were being shipped around the globe.

To some extent the same qualities that make an animal a good stowaway may qualify it for more natural kinds of overseas dispersal, especially for traveling on rafts. Although there can be little doubt that many of the lizards that are widespread members of island fauna got there across water barriers, the exact method of their transportation is not known. The zoogeographer P. J. Darlington believes that winds have been of little importance in distributing island reptiles. Although this is probably quite true, it seems to me that the anole lizards, which are slim, light, arboreal and characteristic of island fauna, might be an exception. But for most island reptiles, raft transportation is surely a more important factor.

It is a shame that the distribution of animals by natural rafts has been so little studied. There are various places in the world where much could be learned by direct observation. The south shore of Trinidad, where flood water from the Orinoco brings in all kinds of raftborne waifs, would be a good place to undertake such a project.

THE ADVANTAGES OF BEING LEGLESS

Long, skinny and legless, a snake can exploit many parts of a habitat better than most four-footed animals. The garter snake of the eastern United States (above) is ordinarily found on stony hillsides near creeks. Its ground-hugging form allows it to move quickly and silently through crevices, decaying leaves, logs or tall grass. In these places it also finds the amphibians and worms that are its prey.

IN the *Pictorial Museum of Animated Nature*, a 19th Century journal in which many wonders are on view, I recently came across an old record of reptile-rafting to St. Vincent—an island some 150 miles north of Trinidad and downstream from it in the Equatorial Current. The item is quoted from the writings of the Reverend Lansdown Guilding of St. Vincent, and though old and quaint it is a rare sort of observation. It sounds authentic, so I offer it here:

"A noble specimen of the boa constrictor was lately conveyed to us by the currents, twisted round the trunk of a large sound cedar tree which had probably been washed out of the bank by the floods of some great South American river, while its huge folds hung on the branches as it waited for its prey. The monster was fortunately destroyed after killing a few sheep, and his skeleton now hangs before me in my study, putting me in mind how much reason I might have had to fear in my future rambles through St. Vincent, had this formidable reptile been a pregnant female and escaped to a safe retreat."

Thus, if the evidence offered by animals is used to reconstruct paleogeographic history, the vagility of the species involved obviously has to be reckoned in, and here reptiles play a particularly important role. Lizards generally are among the most ubiquitous island animals, and although some of their island range is the work of man, much of it is the result of their special tendencies to passive transportation by natural forces. Amphibians, mammals and snakes, on the other hand, are much less susceptible to interisland distribution than lizards. If an observer were to be suddenly transported to an unknown island and a look around revealed a varied assortment of amphibians, snakes and mammals, for example, he could be confident that the place was not far from a mainland shore and that recent connections had existed. But if there were no snakes at all there, and no mammals or amphibians, but instead the place were swarming with lizards, there would be no doubt that it was a far-off island, and very likely a volcanic one with no land bridges in its recent history.

So while one factor involved in the distribution of animals is the distance to be covered and another is the time that has elapsed, a third consideration is the innate ability of the potential colonist to get across the distance. Still another factor, quite as important as the others, is the ability of the animal to survive in the new place when it gets there. No matter how narrow the barrier, how long the time, or how great the dispersal ability of an animal, its spread will finally be limited by the amount of appropriate habitat. In trying to account for the distribution of the fauna of an area it is often not easy to distinguish between the effects of history and ecology.

The three major media of the world—earth, air and water—have all been repeatedly invaded and exploited by the reptiles in many different ways. Most reptiles live on the surface of the ground or in trees; but they are down with the earthworms too, and they glide and parachute about, and once they even very nobly cruised the air.

There is no modern reptile capable of sustained aerial locomotion. The most advanced aerial reptiles that ever lived, the pterosaurs of the Mesozoic, are all extinct. Though perhaps pre-eminently soarers or gliders, they were in some cases surely capable of flapping flight, and may even have fed on the wing, like an albatross or a pelican. The other important—and more lasting—aerial venture during the Age of Reptiles was made by the line that became birds.

Although true flight has been lost to the reptile line, there are many arboreal snakes and lizards in which body weight has been drastically cut down, making it possible for them to fall from great heights without injury. I have many times seen little anoles, while courting or fighting in the trees in my yard, fall from 40 or 50 feet up and suffer no evident damage. In fact, they often scurry straightway to the nearest tree and go up it, as if the incident had not even broken their train of thought. The light-bodiedness of such tree-climbing reptiles is itself an aerial adaptation that enhances survival by checking acceleration before a dangerous speed of fall is reached. From this to parachuting, by spreading flaps of skin, broadened feet and legs, or the rib-supported edges of the body wall to increase buoyancy, is another step along the same adaptive path, and one that has been taken by various modern lizards and snakes. In some of these—notably *Chrysopelea*, the oriental "flying snake," and the lizards of the genus *Draco*—the broad surfaces are so extensive that the fall actually becomes a long glide and the direction of the flight may even be partially controlled by the gliding animal. The whole line of development from the arboreal habitat to aerial locomotion seems such a clear one that the lack of any recent flying reptile is like an incongruous gap.

THERE are not many kinds of living space from which reptiles are absent. Invasions of the soil, for example, have been made repeatedly by unrelated kinds of snakes and lizards, many of which have lost eyes, legs or both in adapting to a burrowing existence. Three different ways of living underground may be distinguished. One is to dig and inhabit a permanent burrow, as monitors and various other lizards and some tortoises do. In these cases, feeding is not subterraneous. The burrow serves only for concealment or for maintaining a tiny set of favorable weather conditions to retire into when it is bad outside. Another way to go underground is to wriggle into and through loose soil or sand. Such sand-swimming is the habit of various kinds of snakes, and of skinks like the Australian sandfish and the little, nearly legless *Neoseps* of central Florida, and of several other kinds of lizards. The sand viper of African deserts shuffles itself quickly into the sand and, incidentally, leaves the black tip of its tail protruding from the surface as a bait for prey. Like burrowing, sand-swimming is more a way to hide or avoid unfavorable physical factors than a means of locomotion. Sand-swimmers are mainly desert animals, for the not surprising reason that deserts are where the most sand is.

The third way to live underground is to live there all the time. The most confirmed subterranean reptiles are the true underground foragers like the blind, mostly legless, amphisbaenian lizards. This bizarre group has inhabited the soil since the days of the dinosaurs. Most of them stay below permanently, and they evidently travel about over considerable distances, finding their food—

HOW SNAKES MOVE

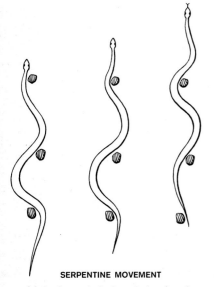

SERPENTINE MOVEMENT

Of the four principal methods of snake movement, the most familiar is serpentine. The body literally swims along in a series of curves which gain traction from exerting pressure against sticks, exposed roots, grass blades, pebbles or slight irregularities in the ground. The snake in the diagram above is using small stones for leverage as it winds forward, and will secure fresh purchases encountering other objects.

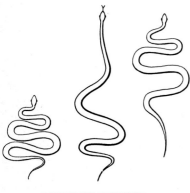

CONCERTINA MOVEMENT

The mechanics of concertina movement are much like those of an inchworm's progress along a branch. At rest the snake's body appears tightly coiled (left). With the tail anchored, the head and neck dart forward (center). Then the neck region grips the ground and the rest of the body is pulled up (right) and again compressed in concertina fashion, in preparation for another fast forward movement of the head.

mostly worms and insects—in the subterraneous habitat. As they move through the soil, they leave tubelike trails behind them, but no one knows to what extent these are re-used as permanent tunnels or burrows.

Little is known of the natural history of subterraneous reptiles. Some 25 years ago, while digging in my yard, I had the vast luck to disinter two eggs of the Florida worm lizard. They were the first ever seen by anyone, but besides that, they were especially interesting because of their extraordinarily long, almost cylindrical shape, because they contained fully formed embryos ready for hatching, and above all because the little lizards in them had conspicuous black eyespots, whereas mature Florida worm lizards are without any sign of eyes at all. In looking through the literature on lizard habits recently, I was surprised to see that in all the years since I found those eggs, no more have been seen by anyone—or at least by anyone inclined to tell of them in print.

One burning question posed by the extreme privacy of the lives of subterraneous reptiles is how the males find the females at breeding time. As in all reptiles, fertilization is internal, and an interlude of mating must be envisioned. But how does it happen, with each worm lizard inching around deep down in the ground and cut off by cold earth from the sight, sound or smell of a prospective partner? No one knows.

Reptiles are well-represented in the desert. Besides the sand-swimmers, there are many that live under rocks and in crevices. Others live in holes in the ground. Very few of these are underground foragers, however, since in deserts there is very little food, either plant or animal, beneath the surface. Most of them are nocturnal and come to the surface to hunt when the sun goes down, although in some cold deserts the regimen is reversed.

A well-made permanent burrow is a limited bit of favorable environment, and various kinds of interloping creatures often are drawn to it and live there more or less in intimacy and harmony. A classic example is the burrow of the gopher tortoise in the southeastern United States, inhabited quite regularly by rattlesnakes, indigo snakes, two kinds of lizards, the gopher frog, various small mammals and a great many insects. Some of these guests go in merely to elude a pursuer. I have often seen rattlesnakes, indigo snakes and foxes barge forthwith into a burrow in which I knew the turtle to be at home. Abandoned gopher burrows are regularly taken over by various mammals as dens. But many occupants of gopher holes—notably some insects and the gopher frog—are true guests, which live intimately with the turtle and have evidently worked out satisfactory ways to keep from being trampled by his comings and goings.

Other reptiles habitually occupy the burrows of various other kinds of animals. Ant galleries and termite nests have special snake and lizard guests. On the dry Pacific slope of Central America much of the reptile fauna can be found at one time or another enjoying the hospitality offered by the burrows of tarantulas, leaf-cutting ants or armadillos.

The range of an animal can be shown on a map. Its habitat cannot. You can plot the distribution of the sort of topography or vegetation or climate in which an animal may be expected to occur, but this would show little about the character of the habitat. A habitat is a place; but it is also the sum of the conditions that make the place easy or hard to live in. These conditions are partly physical and partly biological. Some can readily be seen or measured, but some are subtle or hidden.

In the physical environment of the land one of the clear-cut problems encountered by reptiles, whose ancestors came out of the water, was the danger of drying up. It was this danger that was behind the evolution of the famous shelled reptilian egg, and the same danger imposed the selective pressures that brought changes in the body of the animal itself. It caused reptiles to evolve a horny epidermal covering to cut down evaporation of their body water. This covering, laid on in the form of scales or plates, does not prevent all loss of water. A reptile is perfectly capable of drying up, but the scales do slow down the process to the point where reptiles are able to live in the driest places on earth if they live carefully. The epidermal layer is periodically shed. In snakes and in a few lizards it tends to come off in one piece, the cast skin faithfully reproducing the surface sculpturing of the animal's body, even down to the spectacle over the eyes. In other lizards the skin comes off in patches. In some kinds of turtles the horny scales of the shell surface fall off, but in others they pile up, and unless worn away show peripheral growth rings. In regions with well-marked seasons these rings may be of some value in determining the age of the turtle.

As reptiles pioneered in dry places it was not just the danger of desiccation that they faced. Another big change that fairly slapped them in the face was the wild and capricious temperature regimen of the land. By contrast, water, with its steady daily and yearly temperature cycles, is an easy, even environment. Besides the need to guard against loss of body water the new reptiles had to work out a way to combat the vicissitudes of heat and cold ashore. A long time later their descendants, the birds and mammals, were to do this by balancing high production of metabolic heat with clever radiating devices; but no living reptile is yet able to control its body temperature in this way. For a long time zoologists supposed that reptiles had no control at all over the body temperature, and that it helplessly rose and fell with that of the surroundings. Reptiles were, and until lately have been, spoken of as "cold-blooded" animals.

Now, primarily because of some shrewd researches of R. B. Cowles and Charles Bogert, carried out during the 1940s, this idea has had to be abandoned. Reptiles are not at the mercy of the temperature of the milieu. If they were, they would get very little done, even by reptilian standards. Actually they can maintain a fair control over their blood temperature, and they do this not by controlling gain or loss of metabolic heat, but by moving around, by alternately seeking and avoiding sunlight or warm ground. They practice what is called behavioral temperature control, and some species, at least, maintain their preferred temperature at a remarkably steady level. Not much is known about temperatures in nonbasking reptiles, such as those nocturnal or forest species that would seem shut off from any heat sources except the air or water around them. But the studies of Cowles and Bogert have provided the groundwork for a greatly broadened concept of the habitat of the terrestrial reptile.

Temperature and humidity are only two in a complex system of physical factors that a reptile has to reckon with—to tolerate, to seek or to escape from as it lives out its life. Even if we knew all about all these we would still not know very much about the habitat of the animal, because many of the important characteristics of the habitat—its demands and opportunities—are determined by the living things that share it with the creature one has in mind. Even animals and plants that only very briefly enter the range of a reptile's activities may alter living conditions there.

The most obvious kind of communion between living beings of separate kinds

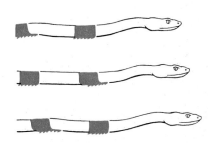

SIDEWINDING

The best way to visualize the looping movement of the sidewinder in sand is to imagine a piece of wire coiled into slightly less than two loops and then rolled along the sand—it will make a series of unconnected oblique tracks like the three in the diagram above. That is what the sidewinder does; it touches the ground at only two points (shown in color) and unrolls its body along the dotted track until its head is extended enough to touch down for the beginning of another loop.

CATERPILLAR CRAWL

Large, heavy-bodied snakes like the constrictors often crawl straight ahead, leaving a track resembling that of a dragged rope. To achieve this motion, the broad, flat belly scales are slid forward. They catch the ground like tractor treads, and allow the rest of the body to be pulled up to them. This action may occur alternately at several points along the snake's body, and is shown in color in these drawings.

is the predator-prey relation. The hog-nosed snake eats a toad and then is eaten by a king snake. A monitor lizard eats the eggs of a crocodile and then one day is eaten by the crocodile that laid the eggs. Of 10,000 sea turtles that hatch on a beach maybe 10, maybe 100 escape bird and mammal predators on the shore and fishes waiting beyond the surf. Such violent interplay among living things is important, but other less violent relationships are perhaps equally so. There are diverse kinds and shades of advantageous contacts, not only among the members of a single species, but also among the various species that share a living place. In the case of every reptile, some time is spent by the sexes in finding one another, courting and mating. Snakes gather for hibernation, turtles mass for migration and breeding, and in each case the function is furthered by the grouping. On the other hand, sharing foraging territory invites combat and strife, so we find that snakes and lizards, and evidently crocodilians and turtles too, tend to stake out, and more or less actively defend as their own, parcels of the habitat. Except for the sexual and territorial behavior of a few species, the whole subject of sociality in reptiles has not been adequately investigated, but enough is known to suggest that there is much to be learned about it.

Just as the individual comes into repeated contact with others of its kind, so the species is always involved in the lives of other species. Most reptiles are carnivorous, and are therefore deeply involved in predator-prey exchanges in their habitats. As has been shown, this brings about various sorts of adaptations that help them to escape being eaten as well as to capture and eat other creatures. Little is known about the more subtle roles and relations of reptiles in their biological environments. They are hosts to various parasites, but none of them lives parasitically. There are lizards and snakes that live exclusively in termite and ant nests, however, and are thus to some extent social parasites. There are not many known cases of beneficial mutualism among reptiles, of useful partnerships between species, although it is likely that more knowledge of the natural history of the group will reveal many cases of casual partnerships and dependencies that are being overlooked now.

Some of the best evidence of the rapport of reptiles with their surroundings is to be seen in the deceptive behavior and resemblances they have evolved. The commonest of these are protective colors, patterns or shapes. The same species may be dark-colored on dark soil and light where light background predominates. Some reptiles—most notably the chameleon—are able to manipulate their coloration to conform to or blend with different surroundings. The most elaborate concealing equipment combines coloration and form, as in three genera of Old World geckos that have greatly flattened bodies and tails, and barklike color patterns. Behavior is often modified to reinforce deceptive resemblances. Various snakes, such as the South American vine snake *Oxybelis*, both look and act like inanimate twigs, vines or lianas. One of these even falls to the ground when touched and lies there like a dead twig. Still other kinds of snakes, including some of the coral snakes and some of the snakes that look like them, manipulate the hind end of the body with considerable verisimilitude as if it were the head end—a maneuver seemingly designed to divert attention from the more vulnerable part.

Along with warning coloration or behavior, some reptiles have developed an ability to mimic warning devices, even though they have no dangerous or unpleasant properties of their own. Some biologists do not believe in the reality of many cases of mimicry. Partly this is because of the lack of laboratory proof of the phenomenon; partly it is because some people lean so far backward to avoid anthropocentric judgments that they fall clear over; and partly the skepticism has been fomented by some real errors of judgment that proponents of the mimicry idea have committed.

For example, I have heard it said that harmless snakes mimic rattlesnakes by vibrating their tails in dry leaves. As Chapter 3 divulged, it is true that many kinds of harmless snakes do vibrate their tails when approached by a potential enemy. But in this particular case, what they do cannot possibly be regarded as mimicry. The wide distribution of the trait suggests that snakes were vibrating their tails to scare off enemies long before there were any rattlesnakes in the world. So what rattlesnakes have done is simply to refine and elaborate an adaptation already entrenched in various snake lines. To be sure, some reinforcement of the widespread tail-shaking habit may occur in snakes living in rattlesnake territory, if only because the rattlesnakes buzz so well and because they back up the warning with such deadly effect. But to think that a black snake is mimicking a rattlesnake when it vibrates its tail is to miss an important point.

One of the sources of controversy is the anthropocentric sound of the word mimicry. The verb "to mimic" seems to some people to carry a taint of volition, and this colors their appraisal of alleged cases of mimicry and makes them suspicious that these are figments of nonobjective interpretation of nature. One of the controversial cases in which even herpetologists are split into camps is that of the so-called mimicking of the gaudily ringed, poisonous American coral snakes by various harmless species. Although often referred to as mimicry, these resemblances are regarded by some zoologists as examples of convergent evolution, in which the coral snakes and their nonpoisonous counterparts have

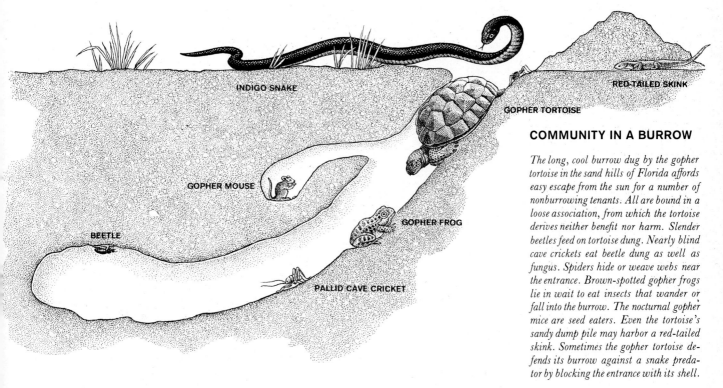

INDIGO SNAKE

RED-TAILED SKINK

GOPHER TORTOISE

GOPHER MOUSE

GOPHER FROG

BEETLE

PALLID CAVE CRICKET

COMMUNITY IN A BURROW

The long, cool burrow dug by the gopher tortoise in the sand hills of Florida affords easy escape from the sun for a number of nonburrowing tenants. All are bound in a loose association, from which the tortoise derives neither benefit nor harm. Slender beetles feed on tortoise dung. Nearly blind cave crickets eat beetle dung as well as fungus. Spiders hide or weave webs near the entrance. Brown-spotted gopher frogs lie in wait to eat insects that wander or fall into the burrow. The nocturnal gopher mice are seed eaters. Even the tortoise's sandy dump pile may harbor a red-tailed skink. Sometimes the gopher tortoise defends its burrow against a snake predator by blocking the entrance with its shell.

developed similar color patterns for some utilitarian reason not connected with warning at all. Some even say that the duplication of pattern is simple coincidence. To support this view it is pointed out that most mammal predators of snakes are color blind, and would evidently not be able to see the ringed pattern as a particularly striking decoration. Moreover, the candystick snakes are all partly subterraneous, spending most of their time beneath logs, in old stumps or actually underground, where little seeing is done by anybody. Still another objection is the occurrence of the ringed coral-snake pattern in harmless snakes living in places where there are no poisonous models around, and hence no conceivable advantage to the deception.

The proponents of the mimicry idea are not persuaded by these objections. They outline their case thus:

(1) There is such a phenomenon as warning coloration. It is widespread among poisonous species, and occurs in animals as dissimilar as frogs, butterflies and the Gila monster. To assume that the poisonous coral snakes are not exhibiting the phenomenon is less acceptable than to say they are.

(2) Although most of both the poisonous and nonpoisonous candystick snakes are indeed secretive and addicted to twilight, none is either wholly subterraneous or truly nocturnal; and in any case the time when they are most in danger of being preyed upon is the interludes when they emerge to the surface, where the color pattern would be in evidence.

(3) Although some snake predators are color blind, others are not.

(4) If coral snakes get any shred of immunity out of being banded with gaudy colors, then, by common sense, this immunity is being shared by the similarly marked scarlet snake and scarlet king snake of the southeastern United States, and by the host of mimics among harmless snakes of the American tropics—at least in areas where a range is shared by a model and a mimic. That some places have "mimics" without models (parts of the United States do, for example) means simply that ranges of animals change through short spaces of geologic time, while color patterns might be expected to persist for a while after their utility has gone.

Or how about this, the mimicry school proposes: The red-shouldered hawk gets about widely, and eats snakes everywhere it goes. If it is one of the predators that instinctively shuns ringed snakes because in some places catching them is dangerous, then might not the same hawk be expected to shun the same pattern in other localities, whether or not any penalty were ever imposed in those places? And so the arguments go on and on.

THESE are some of the most fascinating problems in the field of zoology. They are crying to be studied experimentally, because that is the only way some of the questions involved will ever be answered. And what is worse, so long as they have not been given the glamor of experimental science they will continue to be deprecated by a lot of bright and otherwise sound scientists who ought to be studying them. The whole subject of deceptive simulations, including related behavioral adaptations like bluffing and playing dead, is so broad that it would merit a book to itself. In the single class, Reptilia, there are myriad examples of this one kind of adaptation. They have all come about because they impart increased ability to survive. They are signs of the reality and subtlety of the ecological bonds by which all naturally living beings are drawn into an integrated organization. They are another kind of proof that the habitat is more than a living space, and that no creature ever lives alone.

HUGE EYES, BIZARRE TAIL AND COLORFUL MARKINGS DISTINGUISH THE KIDNEY-TAILED GECKO, A NOCTURNAL INSECT EATER FROM AUSTRALIA

Shaped for Survival

Few creatures have taken to the land with the wholehearted enthusiasm of the reptiles. In desert and jungle, in treetop and burrow and cave they found opportunities for living and exploited them all. This, in turn, led to an extraordinary variety of adaptations—night-seeing eyes like the gecko's above, shapes that hide them, feet to carry them anywhere, even shooting tongues to capture prey.

CHUCKWALLA

SIDE-BLOTCHED LIZARD

GILA MONSTER

SPIN[...]

Melbourne Brindle

WESTERN DIAMONDBACK RATTLESNAKE

The Problem of Heat— and How to Make Use of It

Since its body heat depends almost entirely on outside temperature, the "cold-blooded" reptile would seem to be at the mercy of its environment. Actually, by alternately seeking warmer or cooler areas as needed, a reptile keeps its temperature within the range at which it operates best. This painting shows how

SIDEWINDER

FRINGE-TOED SAND LIZARD

HORNED LIZARD

DESERT IGUANA

CALIFORNIA GLOSSY SNAKE

LEOPARD LIZARD

various Arizona desert reptiles have conquered the fierce heat. The diamondback rattler avoids the sun by lying in a burrow, while the glossy snake buries itself. The leopard lizard, however, hides to escape Gila monsters. Partially digging in, the sidewinder, horned lizard and sand lizard absorb heat from the sand while shielding parts of their bodies from the sun. The other lizards shuttle between sun and shade, and bask at various angles and on various surfaces in an effort to maintain optimum temperatures. The red racer, with a higher heat tolerance, pursues another vital activity—running down food.

A LEAF-TAILED GECKO from Madagascar shows color and markings which blend almost perfectly with the bark and lichen on the tree trunk to which it clings, a disappearing act enhanced by its leaf-shaped tail and the irregular fringes along its flanks. A large and cosmopolitan tribe, geckos are particularly likable for their chirping voices, whose sound is echoed in their name.

A THREE-HORNED JACKSON'S CHAMELEON FROM EAST AFRICA BASKS ON A BRANCH, UNAWARE OF A LATH SHADING PART OF ITS BODY

THE LATH REMOVED THE CHAMELEON SHOWS A BRIGHT-GREEN BAND, DEMONSTRATING THE EFFECT OF HEAT AND LIGHT ON ITS SKIN COLOR

Specialists in the Art of Camouflage

Against the rough bark of the tree on the opposite page a gecko is almost invisible—a striking illustration of how the skin colors of many lizards match their backgrounds. Others can go even further, enhancing the effectiveness of their scaly and irregular shapes by means of dark-brown pigment cells which turn the skin lighter or darker as needed. Chameleons can even change color from gray to brown and green, and sometimes even yellow, in response to various stimuli. The East African chameleon seen above demonstrates its reaction to the changes in heat and light produced by a shadow; others show various hues from night to day, or when angered or alarmed. Lizards are the acknowledged masters of such color-changing. Some snakes have the ability, but use it only rarely and in a minor way.

ON THE ALERT, THE CHAMELEON SWIVELS ITS TURRETED EYES IN EVERY DIRECTION, OFTEN MOVING EACH ONE INDEPENDENTLY OF THE OTHER

Varied Eyes for Varied Lives

Reflecting many different ways of life, the eyes of reptiles show an extremely wide range of adaptations and modifications. For example, the burrowing worm lizard, with little need for any vision at all, has vestigial eyes that appear only as a pair of tiny dots in the skin. But to the chameleon, keen vision is vital for survival, and its eyes are unique in a number of ways. Set on the tips of conical turrets projecting from the sides of the head and protected by eyelids which close to tiny peepholes, they are high-

IN STRONG LIGHT the vertical pupil of the alligator's eye closes to a slit, much like the pupil of a cat's eye. Unlike a cat, however, the alligator's pupil slit appears colorless in the daylight because the backing of its retina is white. But at night *(opposite)* a dramatic change takes place.

94

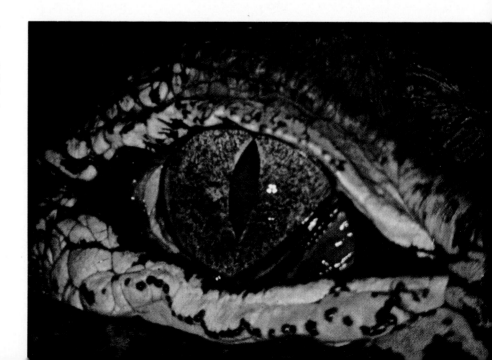

SPOTTING ITS PREY, THE CHAMELEON AIMS BOTH EYES FORWARD, BRINGING BINOCULAR VISION INTO PLAY TO GET ITS VICTIM'S RANGE

ly maneuverable, capable of either independent or coordinated movement, and matchless in estimating distances for the chameleon's swift shooting tongue. Night-prowling reptiles like the alligator, on the other hand, have eyes which are well adapted for seeing in the dark. Geckos show an elaborate refinement for light control. Their vertical pupils have notched edges, which can be brought together to form a series of tiny pinholes. Their separate images are then superimposed at the back of the eyeball.

IN DARKNESS, the alligator's eye glows rosy-pink, a color often attributed to blood lust. Actually, this is the color of a pigment, rhodopsin, which makes night vision possible. Bleached out by daylight, the pigment imparts an eery glow to light reflected from the retina at night.

95

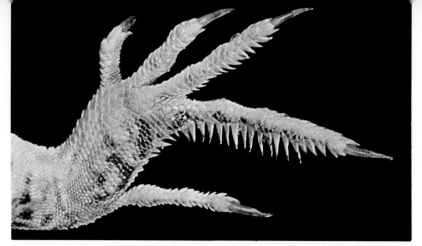

ROWS OF SPINY SCALES on the toes of its hind feet enable the fringe-toed lizard to travel quickly and easily over loose sand. Inhabiting desert areas of the southwestern United States, this reptile also uses its specialized feet to dig in and bury itself.

Feet Which Will Go Anywhere

Carrying their heavy shelters around with them, turtles have no need for speed. Their requirement is for powerful legs able to carry the extra weight, and propel them along at a deliberate pace. Most lizards, by comparison, scurry through life at a breakneck clip. Generally, they use all four legs in moving about, but several can run on their hind legs, like man. The majority of them rely on swiftness and agility to capture prey or escape enemies. Thus, depending on where they live, they have feet adapted for running across soft sand or over rocks or for climbing trees. Arboreal species have by far the most specialized feet: the chameleons have opposable toes which grasp branches like pincers, the geckos have marvelous clinging pads. The snakes, on the other hand, have learned how to move about without any legs at all.

PILLARLIKE LEGS support the weight of the giant Galápagos tortoise, which sometimes weighs 400 pounds or more. While land turtles have developed short thick legs, sometimes with sharp claws for digging, marine turtles have evolved flippers.

CLINGING PADS on the undersides of a gecko's toes allow it to scurry easily up trees and smooth walls and even dash across ceilings. The pads, present in most gecko species, consist of a series of plates which are equipped with many tiny hooklike cells.

TESTING THE AIR, a sidewinder (*above*) flicks its tongue rapidly to pick up microscopic particles for analysis by its Jacobson's organ, a special sensory apparatus aiding its sense of smell.

CLEARING ITS VISION, an Australian naked-toed gecko reaches up with its tongue to wipe the "spectacle" over its eye. More normally, its tongue is also used to pick up and swallow food.

The Many Uses
of Reptiles' Tongues

The flicking tongue of a snake, like that of the sidewinder opposite, is as familiar a part of its popular image as its sinuous leglessness; and indeed, the tongue plays an important role in reptiles' lives. Turtles and crocodilians have relatively simple tongues, but in snakes they are highly modified for two particular services. Forked at the end, they flick rapidly in and out, "sipping" or sampling chemical particles in the air or on the ground, which they then transport to Jacobson's organ, a special chemoreceptor which is not quite for smelling, not quite for tasting, perhaps a little of both. Thus the tongue helps a snake to trail its prey, sample food, sometimes to locate mates. Some rattlers also use it as a warning device, brandishing it stiffly at enemies.

Lizards, by contrast, have unforked tongues which they generally put to the more prosaic uses of picking up, tasting and swallowing food. Some geckos may use their tongues much like windshield wipers, clearing dirt off the transparent coverings of their eyes like the one opposite below, and chameleons employ them in the most dramatic fashion of all, to shoot, immobilize and haul in prey.

TAKING AIM on a fly, a chameleon shoots out its long sticky tongue and scores a bull's-eye. The prehensile tail and tonglike toes keep it firmly anchored. When it is not in use the tongue is bunched up in the throat.

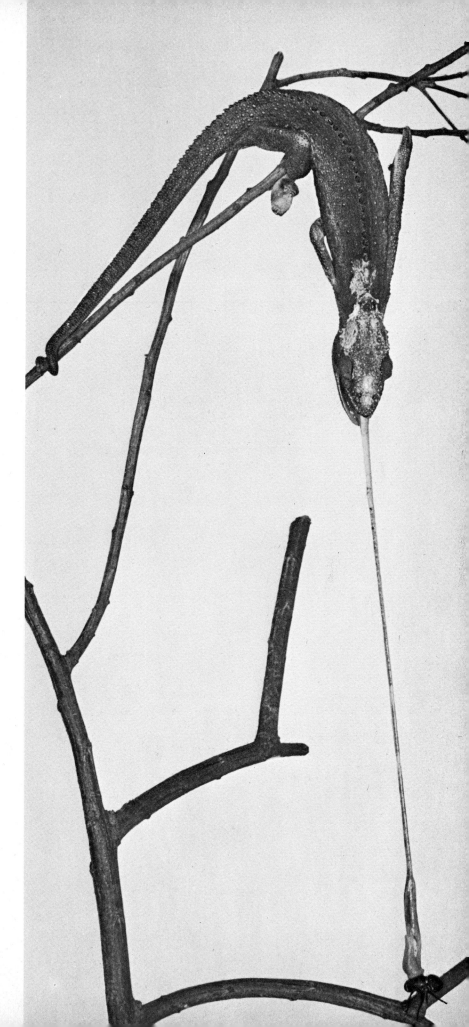

Fancy Footwork without Feet

Evolving from lizards, snakes took an extraordinary course in the matter of locomotion: they developed efficient ways of moving about without any legs at all. Generally they are able to accomplish this in the familiar wavy, or "serpentine," fashion of thrusting sideways with the body, much as a fish swims, with the plates or scales on their undersides finding a purchase against irregularities on the ground (if there are no such rough spots, as on a pane of glass, they cannot move at all). Sometimes, however, snakes glide forward in a straight line—in this case hunching themselves along like caterpillars. Sidewinders hurl themselves ahead in a complicated but efficient fashion by throwing out successive loops diagonally forward. In tree-dwelling species, like the one shown here, the ventral scales are stiffened by transverse keels which give added traction on rough bark surfaces. Bridging a gap from one branch to another, the snake contracts the muscles along the length of its entire body, thus giving it the rigidity of a beam.

LOOSENING ITS COILS, a blunt-headed tree snake prepares to leave the broken end of one branch and bridge the gap to another. Keeled ventral plates and tightly curled tail anchor it firmly.

2. LEVERING THE STIFFENED FORWARD PART OF ITS BODY UPWARD ON ITS COILS, THE SNAKE WINS A PURCHASE ON THE HIGHER LIMB

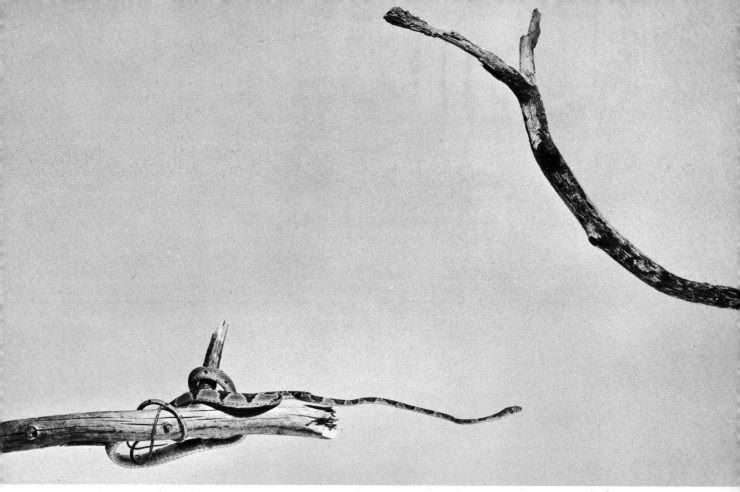

1. TIGHTENING ITS MUSCLES TO ACHIEVE RIGIDITY, THE TREE SNAKE STRETCHES OUT TOWARD THE DISTANT BRANCH WHILE UNCOILING

3. GLIDING FORWARD, IT TAKES IN SLACK BEFORE UNWINDING THE REST OF ITS BODY AND PULLING IT UP FROM ITS FORMER ANCHORAGE

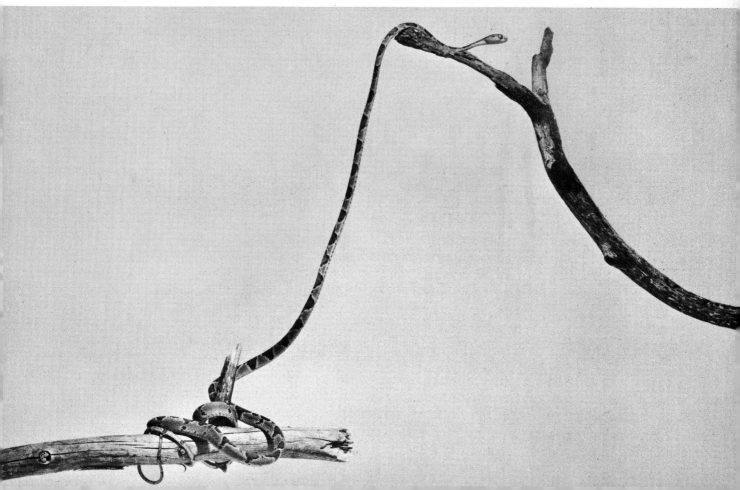

How Snakes Shed Their Skins

Alone among all vertebrates, snakes go through the periodic process of shedding outgrown skin in one elegantly complete operation: when the time comes, they crawl out of the old skin, usually leaving it intact behind. They can do this because they have no limbs or other projections which might inhibit the shedding, and because their outer covering is literally a one-piece suit, from the "spectacles" covering their eyes to the tips of their tapered tails. The process starts a few days before the actual shedding. The snake's skin takes on a dull and lifeless appearance and its eyes cloud over. It also loses its appetite and tends to become irritable. Many species seek water to soak themselves at this time, since they lose a good deal of body liquid along with the old skin. The actual shedding begins when the snake loosens the skin around its lips by rubbing its mouth against a rough surface. This accomplished, it proceeds to work the skin back over its head. Inch by inch, as the snake crawls through brush and over rocks, the thin outer layer is peeled off inside out like a glove. Finally, often in as little as a half-hour, the snake is completely free of its old skin. Resplendent in fresh colors and glistening new scales, it goes on its way, to repeat the process one to six months later when the new skin is outworn.

OPERATION COMPLETED, the snake gleams in its new coat, its body swollen with alarm at being disturbed by the photographer. The dead skin behind it is now attached only by a small section at the tail.

A GROTESQUE MASK, the translucent head part of a cast snakeskin faithfully reproduces each scale and feature of the living snake's head. The creature even sheds its eye coverings along with the sheath of skin.

THE REAR LEGS of an alligator, clearly revealed in this photograph of a swimming specimen, are longer than its front ones, indicating that the crocodilians' land-dwelling ancestors once walked upright.

5

Return
to the
Water

SOMEWHERE in my early schooling, and repeatedly here and there with the passing years, I have heard the grave pronouncement that evolution never reverses itself. I don't know just what this means; but whatever it means, it makes no sense. Evolution may very well "reverse itself," either in hidden biochemical ways or in long-term direction. The statistical odds against a rattlesnake's ever becoming one of the particular fishes in its ancestral background are very great, but there is no rule against the occurrence; and returns and reversals in broad, general trends are common. The loss of legs by reptiles, of which I have spoken at length in other chapters, is an example. Another is the return of land animals to water.

One of the dramatic steps in the evolution of vertebrate animals was the reptiles' shaking free of the water and invading the land. Another important evolutionary advance that reptiles have made, not once but many times, has been to go back to the water again. Calling this an advance sounds like a paradox, a caprice that the newcomer thinking about reptiles is likely to want to have explained. And the explanation is not likely to be of much comfort to him, because the answer is that the returning creatures found advantage in the return, and

SHAPED BY THE SEA

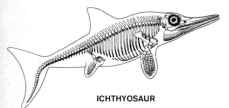

ICHTHYOSAUR

These illustrations of the ichthyosaur (above), an extinct aquatic reptile of some 200 million years ago, and the modern porpoise (below), a marine mammal, show how the environment can shape members of totally different classes into creatures that look very much alike. When the land-dwelling ancestors of these animals returned to the sea, they developed missile-shaped bodies and fishlike fins and tails. Their backbones, no longer required to support a heavy frame, became more flexible, and their pelvic bones almost disappeared.

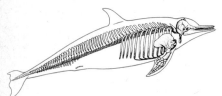

PORPOISE

ways to increase their chances of survival; and that is exactly what attracted them to the land to start with.

Of the three groups of land vertebrates, all have made repeated returns to the ancestral environment. They have gone back to both the sea and fresh water, and their aquatic adaptations range all the way from acquiring a taste for fish to a drastic reforming of the contours, appendages and physiology of their bodies. Although the fossil record is too clouded to tell a great deal about the habitats of ancestral reptiles, it is clear that some of the aquatic reconversions took place at the very beginning of reptile history, while others were made after long periods of specialized living on shore.

There is no doubt that animal life began in the water. Water is the main stuff of protoplasm and it holds in solution most of the other ingredients for life. But besides its suitability as a medium for the primordial chemistry of organic evolution, water has other features that make it continuingly attractive as an environment for the four-footed land animals that left it 300 million years ago. One of these is the stability of its climate. For aquatic animals there is, of course, no evaporation problem at all, and temperature changes, both periodic and sporadic, are far less extreme and rapid than those of the land. Big shifts in atmospheric weather make a slight impression on the weather in the water. The temperature of a lake may change only five degrees in a day during which the temperature of the air is changing 30 degrees. In peninsular Florida it takes several very cold days to bring the water down to 72° along the gulf coast. The green turtles go on grazing on the flats there long after the skinks in the inland hammocks have gone into hibernation.

THE density of water, as compared to that of air, is another of its important qualities as an environment. A good part of the architecture of a land animal goes into structure for mechanical support, and for any animal supported by four legs a body size larger than that of the biggest elephants is mechanically impracticable. Various kinds of creatures did get beyond this size during the Age of Reptiles, but it is probable that they spent a good deal of time standing or wallowing about in swamps and relying on the buoying power of water to help take the burden off their bones. A hippopotamus does the same thing today. In water, considerations of support impose no limits on size—as is graphically shown by the bigger whales and giant squids, and by jellyfish reaching weights of several hundred pounds. Even today, in a time when reptiles are relatively reduced in size, there are some pretty ponderous beasts among the marine turtles and crocodilians.

The same factor that makes it possible to grow to vast size in water imposes a strong limit on speed of travel. To get about slowly in water is easy. One floats and paddles; or one sinks and walks on the bottom. But to cruise the open water requires a drastic remodeling of the terrestrial body. It demands streamlining, and even then there can be no speeds approaching those of birds in the thin air, and only rarely that of a running horse. Water reptiles have adapted to the problems of locomotion in various ways, ranging from the fishlike swimming of the extinct ichthyosaurs and the undulations of the long-tailed, flexible bodies of various species of snakes, crocodilians and lizards, to a great variety of paddling techniques.

One of the fundamental problems reptiles face in the water is carrying out effective respiration there. Most water has oxygen dissolved in it, but a lung is no good for extracting this; and evolving a gill is a complex process which necessitates a remodeling of the circulatory system. No reptile has real gills. Some kinds, however, have converted body surfaces to enable them to extract small amounts of oxygen from the water, and thus are able to prolong their dives. Some turtles, for instance, appear to get some amounts of oxygen from the water through the mucous membranes of the pharynx and cloaca, and probably through the skin as well. Experiments of Dr. Daniel Belkin of the University of Florida suggest that the southern musk turtle is thus able to augment its aquatic respiration, or even dispense with it completely, deriving energy from an oxygenless breakdown of glycogen.

The reptile that commits itself completely to living in the water is faced with the need to make some important adjustments in its methods of reproduction. Reptile eggs drown as readily as the animal that lays them. The two recourses here have been going back ashore to lay the eggs, and bearing live young which are ready to swim and to come up for air. More will be said about this matter in Chapter 6.

ANOTHER aspect of the aquatic environment is the ease and impunity with which it allows a water animal to urinate. This may sound like a trivial matter but it is not. The life processes of animals produce ammonia as a waste, and this becomes poisonous if it accumulates in the body. The ammonia can be converted to less toxic urea and in this form stored for a longer time without harmful effect, but eventually it must be voided. For aquatic animals this is no problem, because both urea and ammonia are soluble, and can be carried away by the simple process of flushing them out, a use of water that reptiles in some land habitats could not afford. Some land reptiles which have to conserve water, like tortoises and terrestrial snakes and lizards, convert their nitrogenous waste to a semisolid state and get rid of it along with the feces, as birds do. To aquatic turtles and crocodilians, however, water conservation is no problem, and they prodigally flush away ammonia, urea or both with water. Although it may never be known for sure, the ichthyosaurs, plesiosaurs and other wholly marine reptiles very likely did the same.

By far the most complete conversion to aquatic life that any reptile ever made was that of the ichthyosaurs, which appeared in the Triassic, reached a peak of abundance and diversity in the Jurassic, and unaccountably declined and disappeared during the latter part of the Cretaceous, when other marine reptiles were still well represented. The ichthyosaur probably lived much as the smaller toothed whales and porpoises live today. Its body was fishlike and drastically molded for swimming, short and torpedo-shaped with a high dorsal fin. The limbs it used on land had become lateral fins. The number of toe bones was greatly increased. Whenever four-footed reptiles or mammals return to the water and become highly modified for aquatic locomotion, they show this increase in the number of toe bones—not in toes, but in the joints of the toes. The bones multiply, shorten and crowd closely together as supports for the guiding plane or paddle that the limb has become. There is little motion between the separate bones—a paddle is no good if it is too floppy. The flexibility they allow is just enough to make a maneuverable surface for propulsion or steering. The ichthyosaurs are the only aquatic tetrapods in which, besides this increase in toe bones, the number of toes themselves has increased, additional ones having been laid down beside the fundamental five that the creature took with it when it entered the sea. As in fishes and dolphins, the neck was short and stiff and the propulsive force of the body was abetted by that of the powerful sweeping tail. This resembled the tail of a modern shark, except that the tip of the backbone turned down into the lower, rather than toward the upper, lobe of the fin. The ichthyosaurs were obviously true marine animals. Many of them may have led a completely pelagic life, and would no doubt have been as helpless on shore as any porpoise or marlin is today.

This makes one wonder how ichthyosaurs reproduced, because they certainly took the reptilian egg into the water with them, and no reptilian egg can withstand immersion. The answer evidently is that ichthyosaurs bore living young. This is not only a logical assumption because of the occurrence of viviparous species among modern reptiles, but it is also borne out by the fossil record. In the black shales of Bavaria, skeletons of pregnant female ichthyosaurs have actually been found. It is too late to hope to know, but I am wondering if a mother ichthyosaur went through the elaborate postpartum behavior that a porpoise does, boosting her newborn young to the top of the water to take its first breaths of air.

The typical ichthyosaur mouth was the usual fish-trap style of jaw—long and slender with many small teeth. Some were toothless, however, and in others the lower jaw was undershot like that of a swordfish.

Besides the interest they hold as the most aquatic reptiles that ever lived, the ichthyosaurs confront paleontologists with two great mysteries. One of these is their strange disappearance during the very heyday of marine reptiles. Although they lived the lives now lived by whales, they were certainly not displaced by their mammalian counterparts, the rise of which came millions of years later. The other thing nobody has ever been able to ascertain about ichthyosaurs is what major reptile group they came from. Some of the older ichthyosaur fossils are a bit more primitive than those of the burgeoning Jurassic stocks, but none gives any clue whatsoever as to the origin of this strange reptilian line.

Another strain of marine reptiles that became adapted to the water in an extraordinary way was the plesiosaurs of the Jurassic and Cretaceous. Plesiosaurs had broad, flattened bodies like shell-less turtles, powerful paddlelike limbs and rather short, finless tails. In some the neck was so long that the animal has been described as a snake threaded through a turtle. They evidently ate fish, but their fishing technique was clearly different from that of the long-jawed, short-necked, many-toothed, fish-eating animals. Old reconstructions of plesiosaurs showed the neck as flexible and swanlike. It is easy to imagine that the

SOME COMMON AMERICAN TURTLES

Compared to the giant sea turtles which weigh many hundreds of pounds, the common American turtles shown here are relatively small, running from a few ounces to a few pounds. The soft-shelled turtle, an aquatic genus, is found in the central and eastern states. Although it spends much time concealing itself in river bottoms, paradoxically it is also fond of basking in the sun. The spotted turtle, easily recognized by the yellow spots on its shell, is also aquatic and lives in the ditches and muddy streams of the East and Midwest.

The common mud turtle, a species found in the East, averages some four inches in length and is the smallest of the turtles seen on these pages. The three-toed box turtle is more adapted to terrestrial life than most other American turtles. It ranges throughout the south-central U.S.

The "red-eared" turtle, which shares the box turtle's range, is the common pet turtle. Readily identified by the small but conspicuous red patches on the sides of its head, it is extremely aquatic, taking to land only for nesting or rare overland migrations. The western painted turtle is one of the most wide-ranging of American turtles. Its upper shell is rimmed with distinguishing red and yellow markings.

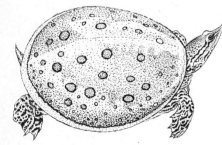

SPINY SOFT-SHELLED TURTLE

SPOTTED TURTLE

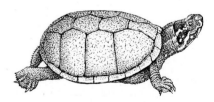

COMMON MUD TURTLE

animal fed by darting movements of its head, by which it plucked fishes from schools. A recent school of thought, however, suggests that the neck was more likely held rigidly out from the body. If so, it is difficult to see how a plesiosaur did its fishing. Jaws at the end of such an inflexible neck could hardly have been swung sideways fast enough to catch any but unwell fishes; and this makes it necessary to suppose that the whole body was maneuvered about in fishing. If so, the ungainly looking plesiosaur must have been a prodigiously athletic animal. Study of the limb girdles shows very broad surfaces for the attachment of powerful muscles for backing movements of the paddles, and perhaps the creature was indeed able to pivot its endless frame on a dime and snatch up astounded herring at the side. Personally, though, not being a paleontologist, I am going to remain skeptical about this modern notion that the plesiosaur's neck was stiff.

The turtles as a group are not truly aquatic, but are really amphibious reptiles. Their primary architectural specialty, the ancient and stubbornly cherished shell that they live in, is typically too heavy for a free-swimming existence. On the other hand, at the low-lying edges of the land where shallow water can be used to help buoy the armored body of a creature that spends its time creeping about the bottom, the shell is a successful device, and the majority of turtles has retained it since the earliest days of the Age of Reptiles. It has been tampered with only by turtles that have strayed from ancestral habits—by the tortoises that went farther ashore, and by a few kinds that have taken almost wholly to the water. In both cases the bony part of the shell has in one way or another been reduced.

THE most aquatic turtle of today is the huge leatherback, or trunkback (*Dermochelys*), which reaches a weight of over 1,500 pounds and has completely shed the bony layer of the shell characteristic of all other turtles. Of the other sea turtles, the green turtle is by far the most highly adapted for swimming. Like the leatherback, it retains the swimming breast stroke even when crossing the beach to nest, while all the other sea turtles walk by moving the legs of each side alternately forward as most four-legged animals do.

Once a male sea turtle goes into the surf after hatching from a nest in the sand, it may never set foot on land again. In a few places in the world, however, green turtles of both sexes do come out on wild shores to bask. I recently visited one of these places—Pearl and Hermes Reef in the Leeward Islands of

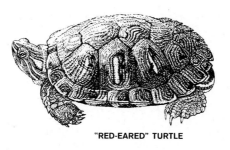

"RED-EARED" TURTLE

THREE-TOED BOX TURTLE

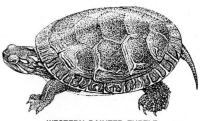

WESTERN PAINTED TURTLE

the Hawaiian archipelago—and saw green turtles and monk seals hauled peacefully out on shore together, flanked by rows of albatrosses. How extensive this basking habit used to be, before the depletion of the world's green-turtle populations, may never be known.

One of the important problems that aquatic animals face is finding their way about the trackless liquid masses of the oceans. A land animal lives surrounded by solid objects that keep their shape and positions and can be used as landmarks for travel guidance. But in the wastes of the water, landmarks are absent or very subtle, and it is hard for a land animal like man to figure out how an aquatic creature keeps from getting lost.

It seems fairly certain that none of the various kinds of marine reptiles simply wanders the oceans at random. The ichthyosaurs, for example, must have systematically cruised the seas on routes and schedules that let them rendezvous with schools of migrating fishes or kept them within the shifting temperature zones in which reptile metabolism goes on properly. If for no other reason, a seagoing reptile needs guideposts to be able to find the opposite sex at breeding time. It will never be known how the reptiles of the past accomplished these guidance feats, but something can be inferred from studying the migrations of fishes, seals, whales and the modern reptiles of the sea: sea snakes, a few crocodilians and above all the marine turtles.

THE fundamental aspect of sea-turtle ecology is that they live in the ocean and nest on land. Little is known about the relation between foraging territory and nesting locality in four of the five kinds of sea turtles. In one kind, however, the herbivorous green turtle, there seems to be a worldwide pattern of commuting between feeding territory and nesting beach. The two phases of the habitat rarely occur close together. Turtle grass grows in expansive stands only in protected water, while good nesting beach forms only where waves come in unhindered and break against the shore. This duality of habitat imposes on the green turtle the need to travel. In many cases the travel covers distances of hundreds of miles in the open sea, but the animals have adapted themselves to this situation to such a degree that they can hold a course through long periods of open-water cruising, and can home to a short section of breeding beach after a thousand-mile cruise in the ocean.

The senses and signals used are not yet understood. About the only advance that has been made in studying them is the realization that the travel is clearly guided by a changing series of signs. The sense of smell is almost surely partly involved. Green turtles—and even more strikingly, ridleys—appear to test and retest the bottom, the washed beach and even the dry sand near the dune front by nosing it in a way that looks like smelling. The same sense may well tell cruising migrants of local changes in the water they swim through, and may allow them to follow smell gradients as homing salmon are thought to do. Little is known of the hearing sense in sea turtles. They make no regular audible sounds themselves, and so are probably not able to piece out their orienting technique by echo sounding of bottom contours, as some fishes evidently do. Incidentally, porpoises, along with their other arresting talents, have been found to squeak at fleeing fishes and determine their direction, range and even kind by appraising the echo that bounces back. The marked structural similarity of porpoises and the extinct ichthyosaurs suggests that the ichthyosaurs, too, may possibly have been echo-locaters; but the truth of this interesting idea will forever remain unknown.

ALLIGATOR OR CROCODILE?

ALLIGATOR

The best way to distinguish an alligator from a crocodile is to look at its head. The alligator has a broader, more rounded snout than the crocodile, and has upper teeth placed outside the line of teeth in its lower jaw. The fourth tooth on either side of its lower jaw is enlarged, but since they slip into a pit in the upper jaw, they are hidden when the mouth is shut.

CROCODILE

The crocodile's head tapers to more of a point than an alligator's, and its upper and lower teeth are pretty well lined up. It too has enlarged teeth on each side of the lower jaw. But they slant outward and fit in a groove outside the upper jaw. As a result, when the crocodile is viewed from the side they can be plainly seen even when the crocodile closes its mouth.

When the known facts of the life history of the green turtle are carefully examined, the conclusion that it is able to navigate is inescapable. Navigation means either using dead reckoning or astronomical signposts—landmarks in the skies. What the green turtle does seems too refined for any known biological mechanism to accomplish through inertial guidance or other kinds of dead reckoning. So it must be that the animal steers by the sun and stars. A few years ago such talk sounded like moonshine. But then the great German zoologist Karl von Frisch discovered the sun-compass sense in bees, and in the following years celestial orientation was shown to guide birds and a long list of other animals, both vertebrate and invertebrate. In the case of sea turtles, it is not yet even known what they are able to see—whether their eyes see more of the night sky than ours, or less, or no stars at all. Even so, to suppose that they get guide signs from the heavens is no longer a bizarre and irresponsible whimsey, but the simplest and most logical theory to explain the facts.

Two important contributions made to the fauna of the waters by the archosaur stock, the ruling reptiles of Mesozoic times, were the phytosaurs and the crocodilians. Unlike the turtles, whose ecological background is unknown but which may never have gone through an interlude as completely land-adapted animals, the crocodilians and phytosaurs appear to have made the return to water after a long period of true terrestrial existence. Their ancestors very likely had acquired the two-legged gait later so widespread among dinosaurs and other ruling reptile stocks.

The phytosaurs and crocodiles are thus both secondarily aquatic and secondarily quadrupedal; and though there are important anatomical differences between the two, they looked alike and surely led similar lives. The phytosaurs were extinct by the Jurassic. The crocodilians live on, although much reduced in diversity. Most of their modern species are amphibious, but there were during the past confirmedly marine kinds, with paddle-feet, narrow jaws, reduced body armor and a high-finned swimming tail.

IN modern crocodilians all degrees of dedication to water life can be seen. A species of Central American caiman crawls far inland in fluctuating ditches, rills and wet meadows, where there is often insufficient water to cover its body. The alligator is more partial to deep water, and may enter the edges of the sea. Crocodiles have definitely entered salt water. One of them, the Asiatic estuarine crocodile, makes long ocean journeys and is known in coastal waters from eastern India and Ceylon to Malaya and Australia. The most inveterate fish eaters among modern crocodilians are the exceedingly slender-snouted Indian gavial (*Gavialis gangeticus*) and the false gavial (*Tomistoma schlegeli*), which more than any other living crocodilian look like the phytosaurs of the Triassic. A difference between them and phytosaurs is the position of the nostrils: in gavials and other living crocodilians they are located at the tip of the snout, but in phytosaurs they were just in front of the eyes.

An important aquatic adjustment of crocodilians is the mechanism they have evolved for keeping water out of their breathing passages when feeding. The feeding process often involves committing mayhem upon intractable prey. The characteristic crocodile feeding technique is to seize a projection of its victim's body, spin on its long axis till the part is twisted off, then take hold again and repeat the grisly process till the prey is all used up. It is important to a crocodile to avoid drowning itself during such wild disorder. Accordingly, the nostrils are located on a pair of bumps at the end of the snout, where they can be thrust above the surface when the animal floats quietly on the water. Air entering them is conducted through two long passages which are separated from the mouth by a bony secondary palate. Just in front of the rear opening of these air tubes a muscular flap projects downward, and this can be pressed against another flap rising from the back of the tongue to make a valve that shuts the mouth off from the breathing passages. At the front end of the tubes the nostrils can also be tightly shut by muscles that work automatically whenever the creature dives. The crocodile is thus able to subdue, dismember and swallow its victims without getting water in its windpipe.

Like the crocodilians, the lizard group has lost its most thoroughly aquatic members. These were three lines of Cretaceous lizards of the group known as Platynota, mentioned earlier as having probably been involved in the ancestry of the snakes. Two of them, the aigialosaurs and the dolichosaurs, were small, long-tailed amphibious lizards whose limbs had in various degrees been converted to paddles. The aigialosaurs were the more primitive of the two and were evidently ancestral to the huge marine mosasaurs, probably connecting their line with that of the monitors. The mosasaurs were thus essentially giant seafaring monitors, with long, finned tails, paddlelike limbs with increased numbers of digital bones, and elongate, very toothy jaws. Most of them probably preyed on fishes and other reptiles, but some had heavy blunt teeth that seemed suitable for smashing the shells of mollusks.

Today the water reptiles, those that are committedly aquatic as well as those that are only partially so, live in every part of the water environment. Some are exclusively marine, some live in fresh water, some are confined to brackish water, and still others are able to pass casually between land and water or between fresh water and the sea.

A survey of the partly adapted modern water reptiles suggests some of the ways by which the rapprochement with water was probably originally made. Many newly marine reptiles of today have gone into the sea via fresh water. Those still partial to fresh water may live there semipermanently, or may enter water only to get food or to hide. Various lizards combine arboreal habits with aquatic interludes, like the tree iguana of the American tropics, which is nearly always found in trees over water, and the lizard *Lophura amboinensis* of the Malay and Philippine Islands. So do a great many kinds of snakes. This is what one would expect of creatures that have acquired their aquatic tendencies where forests are threaded by streams in which they can find refuge or food.

THE seeming paradox of the reptiles forsaking their hard-won place on land and sinking back into the sea—which is really no paradox at all—is heightened by the realization that one of the advantages drawing the animals back is one that helped bring them ashore to start with. The first stage of being either a land animal or a refugee in the water is to live in the shore zones, the swamps, marshes and tidal flats between water and land. At times these places are richer in food than either the land or the ocean. Even today you see the appeal of the fringe zones for terrestrial and aquatic creatures; they are drawn in from both environments for the sporadic and periodic harvests. Their presence in this in-between zone opens paths for natural selection in either direction.

One of the most important food resources offered by shores is their crustaceans. Lizards and snakes of many groups visit or inhabit salt beach or sea cliff for the wealth of crustacean food that may be concentrated there. A Javanese rear-fanged snake, *Fordonia*, has venom specially adapted for killing the crabs that the snake eats—so specialized that it is harmless to fishes and frogs. In Australia and the Sunda Islands several kinds of skinks catch crabs on rocky coasts. Among lizards the skinks are especially prone to venture into seaside habitats, especially in the Indo-Pacific—on Sunda Island one skink even chases fishes in the salt water of mangrove swamps.

Of the lizard-snake group, the most aquatic modern representatives are the cobralike sea snakes of the Indo-Pacific. All the species of sea snakes are marine except one, which occurs in a fresh-water lake on Luzon in the Philippines. These snakes have nothing to do with the sea serpents of fable, nor even with the origin and evolution of the sea-serpent idea. The legends more likely grew out of inadequate observations of oarfish, giant squids or other sea monsters seen piecemeal among the waves by impressionable medieval eyes. The real sea snakes are not over nine feet long—most of them are smaller. They have flattened tails and a compressed body. In most of the species the belly scales are not laterally broadened as in ordinary snakes, but are the same all around the body. Sea snakes thus lack one of the important adjuncts to terrestrial serpentine locomotion, and when they are placed on land they can only squirm and flounder about in a pitiable way. The nostrils are placed on the upper surface of the snout and can be closed by valves. The left lung is reduced, and the right one is greatly elongated, in some cases reaching as far back as the anus. Besides its function in respiration, this long lung is believed to serve as a hydrostatic organ—an interesting parallel with the development of the swim bladder of the bony fishes, which also is derived from a sac originally used by its ancestors as a sort of lung.

SEA snakes eat fishes, principally eels. Some of the fishes they swallow have spines, and instead of digesting or voiding these by natural channels the sea snakes get rid of them by pushing them out through the body wall. This sounds like a dismally unpleasant habit to me. Fresh-water snakes do the same thing occasionally, but evidently only by accident. I have personally seen two water snakes that had been killed when the still-attached spines of a swallowed fish had stuck through the wall of the body.

Sea snakes are as thoroughly aquatic as the leatherback turtle, but in one important way they go beyond the leatherback in adaptation to the water environment. About three quarters of the species are not bound to go back ashore to reproduce, but stay in the sea and give birth to their young alive. In the chapter on reproduction it will be shown that the switch from egg-laying to live-bearing is not quite so earth-shaking an evolutionary event as it might seem. It can be accomplished in various makeshift ways. It has happened repeatedly in many kinds of animals that lead lives in which eggs are at a disadvantage in the environment of the adult. So the wonder is not so much that three quarters of the species of sea snakes bear living young, but that the leatherback, which has been in the water since the Cretaceous at least and possibly from as far back as the Triassic, should still cling to the awkward and hazardous nesting trips to the alien land.

Although the poison of sea snakes is specifically adapted to subduing the fishes it eats, it is also virulently poisonous to warm-blooded animals. Their venom is reckoned stronger than that of any other kind of snake, except possibly the tiger snake of Australia. They are timid and easygoing, however, and rarely bite anybody. There seem to be no records of a sea snake attacking anyone swimming or diving, and wherever they are commonly caught in nets, either accidentally or to supply the Asiatic markets, they are handled with indifference.

There are about 50 different kinds of sea snakes found throughout the tropical Indian and Pacific Oceans. One species, the common black-and-yellow sea snake (*Pelamis platurus*), is pelagic, feeding on fishes in the surface regions of the sea. It wanders as far from the central sea-snake range as the east coast of Africa and the Pacific coast of the Americas.

After wanting for decades to catch a sea snake, I finally came upon three of them one day while looking for ridley sea turtles off the Pacific coast of Mexico in Sinaloa. The snakes were lolling idly at the surface as if sleeping in the sun. They looked absent-minded and easy to catch, but when I swept mightily with a long-handled dip net, each in turn darted straight down and, one by one, I lost them all. Then only last month my son Steven met a man carrying a live sea snake on a beach on the Pacific coast of Costa Rica. The man was going to use it for bait. Steven was tempted to buy it and bring it home but thought it might irritate officials along the way. The man let him hold the snake, however, and Steven tells me it felt soft-skinned and rubbery and not at all the way snakes generally feel.

The water snakes of the subfamily Homalopsinae include about 10 genera, some of which are wholly aquatic. They range from India and China to Australia and the Philippines and are found in both fresh and salt water. They eat fishes and are able to swallow their food when they are submerged. Their nostrils are crescent-shaped, and like the sea snakes they have valves that shut when they go under water.

Among modern snakes there is a continuous spectrum of adaptations between terrestrial and aquatic extremes. The water snakes of the genus *Natrix* usually use the water for feeding and concealment, but spend much of their time basking on the branches of overhanging trees or bushes. Some snakes, such as the black swamp snake (*Seminatrix*) and striped swamp snake (*Liodytes*), emerge from the water only rarely. In the water they do little swimming, however, but instead crawl about among masses of floating water plants, foraging for crayfish and other little water animals.

AMONG lizards the most striking aquatic representatives of modern times are the big, gregarious marine iguanas that eat algae on cliffs on the Galápagos Islands. Perhaps just as confirmedly aquatic, if not even more so, is the South American caiman lizard (*Draecaena guianensis*), which lives in tidal marshes of the Guianas and the lower Amazon. It eats snails and mussels, the shells of which it crushes with flat-topped teeth. A relative in northeastern South America is the brown water lizard, *Neusticurus rudis*, an expert swimmer that catches fishes, tadpoles and aquatic insects in forest-bordered streams. Nilotic monitors dive from the banks of East African rivers and seem almost as aquatic as the crocodiles that often slide in with them.

So, the reptiles no sooner got the hang of things on land than they went back to the maternal sea again. They did not go back as fishes or amphibians, but as reptiles. They returned to the ancestral medium with reptilian lungs and scales, still producing shelled eggs that had to be laid on shore. Their return to water was not a degeneration, any more than snakes' losing their legs was degeneration. It was a positive and profitable adaptation of plastic new stocks to an old environment. The environment they returned to was the primordial cradle of life, but it offers opportunity to advanced forms of life as well. It still holds strong attraction for all beings built of protoplasm, no matter what their commitments to the dry parts of earth may be.

BABY GREEN TURTLES, SHOWN SLEEPING ON THE WATER, THOUGH HATCHED ASHORE WILL SPEND ALMOST THEIR ENTIRE LIFETIME IN THE SEA

The Aquatic Reptiles

After freeing themselves of a dependence on water by evolving a shelled egg that could be deposited on land, many primitive reptiles did an about-face and splashed back in. All major groups of modern reptiles, with the exception of the tuatara, now have their amphibious or completely aquatic species. Among these are snakes so specialized for life in the seas that they never venture ashore.

AN AMERICAN ALLIGATOR SHOVES OFF FROM A RESTING PLACE ON A RIVER BED. USING A SWIMMING METHOD OF ALL THE CROCODILIANS, IT

The Many Attractions of Water

Different reptiles utilize the water for different purposes. The amphibious crocodilians use it to swim and hunt in. They also use it to cool off, for though found in warm climates they cannot tolerate great heat since they have little control over their own temperatures. If exposed for a long time to the hot-test rays of the sun without water for a dip close by, a crocodile will die. Not unexpectedly the strong crocodilians are proficient swimmers, employing either the high-speed method shown above or a slow paddle. The only modern marine lizard is a species from South America's Galápagos Islands. It lives

THE SIAMESE SWAMP SNAKE HAS A GREEN CARPET OF ALGAE ALL OVER ITS BODY, MAKING IT INVISIBLE TO THE SMALL FISHES THAT IT EATS

TUCKS ITS LEGS AND WEBBED FEET AGAINST ITS SIDES AND SURGES FORWARD WITH UNDULATIONS OF ITS POWERFULLY MUSCLED TAIL

along the shores and enters the water to feed on marine algae, rarely venturing out into swift currents. It has evolved a powerful flattened tail for swimming, and strong clawed legs for climbing back up on the volcanic cliffs that are its base of operations. Among the most aquatic of the reptiles are the big sea turtles; some species are able to swim as fast as a man can run the 100-yard dash. Most sea snakes live out their entire lives in salt water, feeding on fishes. The Siamese swamp snake at left spends a lifetime in fresh water unless dragged out of it, at which point it stiffens up like a board.

THE MARINE IGUANAS OF THE GALAPAGOS ISLANDS ARE SKILLFUL SWIMMERS AND DIVE INTO WATER AT LOW TIDE TO FEED ON SEAWEED

GOOSE BARNACLES growing on the head of a sea snake are a potential hazard, sometimes covering an eye, as here. The snake sheds them with its skin.

Submersible Snakes

Most snakes can swim, but none are better equipped for it than the poisonous sea snakes with their paddlelike tails and laterally compressed bodies. They inhabit the warm waters of the eastern and western Pacific and the Persian Gulf, and are often seen swimming a thousand miles or more from shore. Some can even swim backwards. A factor enabling many of them to lead a completely aquatic life is their habit of giving birth to living young, thus freeing them of the necessity of ever leaving the water to deposit eggs on shore as the sea turtles must do. Most have dispensed with the enlarged abdominal plates used by land snakes in locomotion. Although all sea snakes must surface to breathe, they can stay submerged for long periods—apparently by extracting the oxygen they need directly from the water.

A SEA SNAKE from southeast Asia shows the typical conformation of many of its kind—a heavy body, with a tiny head and flattened tail. In several species the body is four to six times broader than the head.

A RIVER SNAKE, the South American anaconda is an expert swimmer and prefers to stay in water, though it is also adept on land. It feeds on many aquatic animals; one 25 feet long contained a six-foot caiman.

MOUTH AGAPE, an alligator snapper, largest of North American fresh-water turtles, extends its wiggling lure—a wormlike outgrowth of the tongue—and waits for fishes to nibble at it.

When thus employed, the whitish or light-gray lure pinkens. The algae covering the shell help disguise the head in murky water and may also inveigle prey into coming closer to the lure.

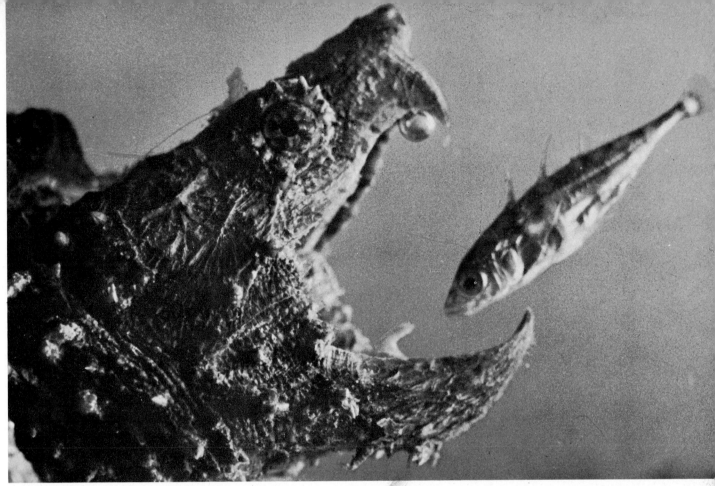

DARTING TOWARD THE BAIT, a fish enters the mouth of the alligator snapping turtle. Instantly *(below)* the jaws snap shut and manipulate the fish into a swallowing position. If the fish were larger, the turtle would first tear it apart with its clawed front feet. The alligator snapper probably forages mainly at night and reserves the lure for occasional use during the sunlit hours.

A STRETCHABLE NECK, ALMOST AS LONG AS ITS SPINE, ALLOWS A SUBMERGED MATAMATA TO DRAW IN AIR THROUGH SNORKEL-LIKE NOSTRILS

The Matamata, the Weirdest Turtle

The river-dwelling matamata of northeastern South America looks like one of evolution's mistakes. But its most bizarre features are the ones that serve it best. A cautious, extremely slow-moving predator of small fishes, it lurks on the murky bottom, camouflaged by a mottled greenish-brown skin and a ridged shell festooned with algae. The ear flaps and tabs on the head and neck are movable and act as fish lures. The long neck serves to thrust the tube-like nose out of the water for air, and also as a means of approaching quarry while the body remains almost motionless. When danger threatens, the neck cannot be retracted into the shell in the manner of most other turtles, but is curled under the carapace.

LYING IN AMBUSH, a matamata halts its movements as an unwary knife fish, attracted by waving lappets of flesh fringing its arrow-shaped head, swims closer and closer to its ready mouth.

SUDDENLY OPENING ITS JAWS and expanding its neck, the matamata creates a vacuum that sweeps the fish into its mouth with the inrushing current. Later on, it will expel the water.

THE FACE OF THE MATAMATA suggests an advancing army tank. The nose extends forward over the broad, V-shaped mouth, as do the tiny eyes. The fleshy jaws, which open into a hoop, lack the horny edges of other turtles' mouths since the matamata does not chew its food. Walking behind the head and swiveling neck is the rest of the body, covered by a lumpy shell.

6

The Miraculous
Shelled Egg

REPTILES are sexual animals and are the group that introduced internal fertilization to the vertebrate line. Thus, in a manner of speaking, they laid the foundation for the family unit in higher vertebrates, and from this came human society itself, with all its excitement and troubles. The ancestral amphibians deposited their eggs virtually naked in the water, and fertilized them by simply releasing sperm in the general vicinity. The hazards of such an informal operation to both sperm and egg are obvious. The reptilian egg, however, enters the world already fertilized, and packaged against a certain amount of environmental adversity. One need only compare the dozen or so eggs laid by the average lizard with the thousands laid by toads to see the great economy the new method has brought.

But even an egg with a shell is delicate. It can incubate successfully only within a narrow range of conditions of temperature, humidity and concealment. It is thus not surprising to find that a few reptiles have independently hit upon the recourse that we think of as one of the main attributes of the mammals—that of producing living young.

All the live-bearing reptiles of modern times are lizards and snakes. Turtles and crocodilians produce only eggs, and so does the tuatara. It is significant that of the three reptiles which venture farthest north, even across the Arctic Circle, two—the European viper and the lizard *Lacerta vivipara*—bear their young alive. So does the slowworm *(Anguis)*, another venturer into northern regions. The cold ground of those areas, no doubt, is not well suited to incubating eggs. Neither is water, so far as shelled eggs are concerned, which explains why most reptiles with strongly aquatic habits also bear their young alive.

Many of the live-bearing reptiles, however, belong to groups that have egg-laying members too. The skinks, the lacertas, the boids and the vipers are examples. There are even species that lay eggs in some parts of their ranges but bear live young in other parts. This suggests that their viviparity—as the ability to produce live young is called—is not so formal an undertaking as it is in mammals, and this is true. Some reptiles merely keep the eggs inside the body for varying periods up to and after hatching time. In others there are extensive, placentalike connections with the tissues of the maternal oviduct. In one type the yolk sac is merely plastered against the wall of the oviduct, and is used primarily for respiration. In a more advanced type the embryonic membranes, the chorion and allantois, interfold with maternal tissues and the embryo not only gets water and nourishment as well as oxygen, but conveniently has its excretory wastes taken away too. None of the live-bearing reptiles has dispensed with a big store of yolk as the main source of nourishment for the growing embryo.

Although lizards do not fare well in cold climates, the Common Lizard of Europe has a wide range, and has become adapted to life in northern latitudes by bearing its litter of young alive (above), keeping the developing eggs as warm as possible by incubating them inside its body. In warmer regions farther south, however, females of the same species (below) produce their young by laying eggs to hatch.

ALL reptiles practice internal fertilization. In all modern forms except the tuatara the male has an organ kept turned outside in, in the base of the tail, and everted through the opening of the cloaca during erection. In the tuatara the transfer of sperm is accomplished by bringing the genital openings into contact, as in birds. This was probably the method used by the ancestral reptiles—it is clear, in any case, that the penis had separate origin in turtles, crocodilians and mammals on the one hand, and in lizards and snakes on the other.

Thus, male lizards and snakes have not just one, but a pair of hollow structures called hemipenes, which make up their copulatory organs. Located as they are in the tail just behind the opening of the cloaca, the hemipenes often give the tail of the male a thicker, more gradually tapering contour than that of the female, and in many species the sexes can be distinguished by this difference. A groove that serves as a channel for the sperm extends from the opening of the sperm ducts along the inner wall (which is the outer wall during erection) of each hemipenis, and the surface may be pleated or set with spines that keep it in place in the oviduct of the female during mating. Either one of the hemipenes may be used, but only one, the one nearest to the female, is everted and protruded from the cloaca during erection, which is brought about by a combination of muscular action and distension of the walls with blood.

Among different reptiles fertilization is scheduled differently with respect to the time of nesting. In most species it seems to occur, as might be expected, just before the eggs are laid; but in some the sperm may live on in the reproductive tract of the female and continue to fertilize eggs months or even years after copulation has taken place. The longest known periods of such deferment of fertilization are four years for the diamondback terrapin of the southern United States, and five years in the case of the tropical American cat-eye snake. The green turtle, which evidently mates only in the sea off the nesting beach, often does so *after* the female has gone ashore and laid her eggs. Since a given female makes her migration to the nesting ground only once in three, or more rarely two, years, it seems probable that sperm must regularly be stored for that length of time between nesting journeys.

In at least two races of lizards there appear to be no males at all, and young are evidently produced from unfertilized eggs. Such reproduction is known as parthenogenesis, or virgin birth. The most familiar case of parthenogenesis is that of the honey bee. The queen lays two kinds of eggs, some fertilized, some unfertilized. The unfertilized eggs produce the males, or drones; the fertilized eggs produce the workers. Ants, wasps and various other invertebrate animals sporadically or periodically reproduce by parthenogenesis. In some cases the parthenogenetic stage occurs at a time when conditions in the environment would make it difficult for the two sexes to meet for mating. How the two lizards evolved the practice, and why, is not clear. In some other species of lizards the females greatly outnumber the males and it is possible that this same phenomenon of parthenogenesis may normally alternate with bisexual reproduction.

Because the genitalia of male reptiles are internal, it is not always easy to tell the sexes apart. It takes a real expert, for instance, to determine the sex of a snapping turtle or alligator. However, in most species there are certain external features by which it is possible to distinguish the sexes of fully mature individuals. The two most obvious ones are size and coloration. There is no set rule about which sex may be the larger, but in many species it is the male that is bigger than the female. Where difference in color patterns exist, it is generally the male which has the more vivid coloration, as is usual in birds; but here again the situation is sometimes reversed. In some species the sexual coloration is a sort of nuptial dress, assumed for breeding and later abandoned.

Internal fertilization is a cooperative process, and to bring it about the sexes must find each other, and must be physiologically prepared for mating. Most if not all reptiles show some sort of courtship behavior by which the sex of a potential partner is determined, the coyness of the female is overcome, and a readiness to mate is generated in both members of the pair. Courtship often duplicates or blends with the expressions of rivalry and home defense between males, and since this whole complex of innate behavior is a hereditary part of the make-up of a species, it affords an interesting field for study.

THE courtship of a number of different snakes and lizards is a case in point. Although there are clear similarities in behavior patterns among the two groups, it has been found that most lizards recognize the female visually, while snakes depend on odor, trailing the female with their noses as well as with the tongue and Jacobson's organ. Male lizards put on quite a display among themselves—showing colored throat fans, erecting crests, arching their necks and affecting various gaits—but how much of this actually carries over into courtship is not surely known. Some of it, however, is brought to bear by the male on a prospective partner. When the female is thoroughly recognized as a female and her reticence overcome, the male lizard (like the males of some snakes) seizes her with his jaws, bends the base of his tail downward to maneuver the cloacal openings into contact, and insertion of one of the hemipenes is effected.

Turtles, both aquatic terrapins and land tortoises, carry out varyingly elaborate courtships which may include butting and nipping of the female by the male, or his swimming backward in front of her, fluttering his claws beside her face, or stroking her cheeks with his elongate fingernails. Among some species of pond turtles and among sea turtles, courtship is accompanied by competitive behavior among males. Two males, on rare occasions even three, may attempt to court the same female simultaneously and combine this with a mild struggle among themselves. In the pond in front of my house, during the mating season of the pond cooters, turtle heads are regularly seen in threes or fours. Off and on, for as long as two or three days at a time I have watched groups of these heads with a spotting scope, and while I could see little of what the bearers of the heads were actually doing, it did not seem to involve any very violent strife. The three heads simply stayed together in a restricted patch of water for a day or more at a time, and there were occasional outbreaks of splashing and finally the back of one of the turtles would come out of the water, indicating that mating was taking place.

A similar thing occurs among the green turtles at their nesting ground on the coast of Costa Rica. Here, too, the observations made have been only in snatches, and whatever subtleties of courtship behavior are carried out have not been seen. But during the early part of the nesting season the turtles mate out in front of the beach a few hundred yards beyond the surf line. For the first week or so of the mating time there are large numbers of courtship groups involving two males and one female. Among sea turtles, mating is a strenuous process. Attempts of the male to mount the back of the female involve a great deal of thrashing and splashing of water. Once the male attains the position on the upper shell of the female, however, he remains firmly anchored by two huge claws on his front flippers which grip the fore edges of her shell, and by a strong horn at the tip of his tail which curls up under the back edge of her shell. The only time male turtles are seen on shore at the nesting ground is when a copulating pair is caught by a breaker and thrown onto the beach.

The courtship of the alligator is noisy and exciting. The bull bellows and exudes musk from glands on the throat and at the sides of the cloaca. When the female approaches, the two of them race about in wild circles, making a big wake that rocks the reeds and sends the fishes flying. The frogs stop singing and the waterfowl scream.

Closely related to courtship is rivalry and combative behavior among males. This sort of strife is not generally disorderly and injurious, but actually may serve a variety of useful purposes. It keeps the race physically on its toes, as it were, weeding out the weaker individuals as breeders. It brings about a distribution of territory, and thus lends order to both the reproductive process and the daily life of the individual. It establishes hierarchies of dominance and submission, and these again contribute harmony by forestalling more harmful untrammelled fighting. And just as courtship does, the fighting may help instigate glandular cycles involved in the mating process.

IN some species a by-product of fighting between males is to augment their often fuzzy capacity to recognize the female at mating time. Experiments show that when breeding males of certain lizards approach another of their kind, their mode of sex recognition is not, as one would expect, to search for signs of femininity. Instead, the criteria seem wholly negative: if the challenged lizard fights back it is a male; if not, the only alternative is to regard it as a female lizard and make appropriate overtures.

In many cases the contests between males are carried out without physical contact. The same ends are accomplished by various kinds of signals, posturings, and flashings of color patches, such as the throat fans of some lizards. The magnificent bellow of the American alligator, though not thoroughly understood, is partly a sexual call, but is partly used also as a territorial challenge.

A pattern of ritualistic sexual behavior quite as elaborate as that of some birds is the "combat" dance of some male snakes. The distribution of this extraordinary habit among the various snakes of the world is not accurately known, but it is found in a variety of species and genera—in snakes as unrelated as the rat snakes and the vipers, for instance. The exact aim of the dance is not known either. It may be prenuptial rivalry, or it could be a ceremonial way of contesting territory. I first saw this dance performed by a pair of cottonmouth moccasins years ago, and it still ranks as one of the most elaborate and stylized animal ceremonies that I have ever witnessed. It can best be compared to some of the most advanced ballets of birds.

It happened in 1941. My wife and I came upon the snakes in an open pool at the edge of a marshy lake in Florida. We were at once struck with the realization that something untoward was going on, and so sat quietly, watched raptly, and soon began taking notes and making sketches of the figures of the dance.

Throughout we were laboring under the mistaken impression that it was courtship we were witnessing, and because in a number of mated cottonmouth pairs that I had previously come upon the male was the smaller, I quickly decided that the smaller member of the dancing pair was the male in this case too. When the dance was over we took our notes and sketches home and wrote a little description that was later published in a zoological journal. In spite of our somewhat fundamental misapprehension regarding the sexes of the snakes, the description of the dance was faithful, and rereading it for the first time in 10 years brought it vividly back to mind.

WHEN first observed the snakes were gliding slowly about the pool, the forward third of their bodies raised high, crossed and interlocked in an open, symmetrical half-twist. The two heads, side by side, were bent downward at a slight angle to the necks, which were held almost vertical. The eyes stared out into space in a vacuous way suggestive of some sort of cataleptic seizure. Every few seconds the two snakes rapidly and in perfect synchronization smoothly recrossed their necks, reversing the relative positions of their bodies. Although there was little or no contact between the exposed portions of the bodies during this maneuver, the rhythmical precision of the reciprocal movements was such that it seemed as though two like parts of a single body were involved. From time to time the two would pause in their gliding traversal of the pool and in one place execute and reverse their figure eight several times before moving forward again.

After five minutes of such activity the smaller snake disengaged itself. Swimming slowly around the other two or three times, he inspected the raised forepart of his opponent's body minutely, touching it repeatedly with the tips of his tongue or with the end of his snout. Finally, he circled to the rear, looped himself across the partially submerged portion of the body of the other snake and shuffled and slipped himself slowly forward. On reaching the elevated thoracic region of the other, he threw a tight loop of his neck around it and began a spiraling climb upward. During this procedure the larger snake seemed intent on raising his head as high as possible above the water and, aided in this effort by supporting loops of the body of the other, he succeeded in reaching a height of at least 17 inches for a brief time. When the lesser combatant had enfolded the other in two complete loops, and the heads of the pair were at nearly the same level, the rigid body of the big snake suddenly relaxed and yielded symmetrically to the enveloping coils of his opponent.

Thus intertwined, and with their heads posed almost vertically high above the surface of the water, the pair began what appeared to be a frantic and concerted effort to climb out of the water. At the same time the interlocked bodies swayed slowly back and forth, each backward swing being more extreme than the preceding. After some 60 seconds of this, the combined upward struggling and backward rearing carried the snakes beyond the point of balance and they fell over in a tangle of writhing coils.

This extraordinary operation was repeated three times, and in each instance, after the final collapse, both snakes would suddenly emerge to a third of their lengths, one two inches behind the other, with their snouts pointed upward. For from one to three minutes they would pose thus, all the while vibrating synchronously back and forth through an arc of about half an inch. At this time the posterior two thirds of the bodies, which until now had been submerged and presumably intertwined, floated high in the water, side by side, motionless except for deep and rapid breathing.

AFTER 45 minutes the big snake suddenly disengaged himself from the neck-loop of the other, circled the pool once and then struck out at top speed through the cattails in a series of zigzag rushes. For perhaps 30 seconds the snake left behind remained motionless in the center of the pool, watching the antics of his erstwhile partner. When one of the mad dashes of the swimming snake carried him to the edge of the open water, the one left in the pool appeared to realize the danger of losing contact permanently and set out in pursuit.

Then there was a wild chase through the emergent vegetation, far out into the open water and back to shore again, with the smaller snake apparently having no trouble following, at a distance of six to eight inches, the erratic course taken by the larger one. After about five minutes, however, the race terminated abruptly when the big snake plunged through a dense sheaf of dead *Typha* leaves, crossed an open pool and concealed himself in a hassock.

This tactic seemed to baffle the other completely. He dashed about excitedly for a moment and then settled down to a deliberate and methodical search for the trail. Very slowly he cruised a strip of some 50 yards of the lake margin, quartering the zone of vegetation, and thrusting his snout into piles of trash and clumps of *Typha*. He vibrated his tongue continuously, flicking its tips against plant stems and floating sticks and into the water itself in a vain attempt to straighten out the intricate course.

We watched the fruitless search for some 30 minutes. Then the sun began to set and a cold rain started falling. When we left, the unpromising search was still going on.

Although the literature of that time had little to say about this most extraordinary of reptile rituals (and what there was mistakenly interpreted it, as we did, as courtship), similar behavior has now been observed both in the field and in reptile houses, in a number of species including rattlesnakes and colubrids. That a comparable set of complex stereotyped dance figures should have been clung to through all the time since rat snakes and rattlesnakes diverged seems extraordinary. That the same ceremony should have been carried over by the cottonmouth into the water is even more imposing evidence of genetic stability, or of utility, or of both. The comparative study of such behavior is the material of the burgeoning new field of natural history called ethology.

Practically all the eggs laid by reptiles are spherical or elliptical in shape. Those of snakes and lizards usually have flexible shells; those of crocodilians are hard-shelled, and the shells of turtle eggs may be either parchmentlike or like glazed or unglazed porcelain. The eggs laid by a reptile at a given nesting may number from the two or three of the striped mud turtle (there is some indication that the African soft tortoise lays only a single egg) to the 150 or more of the hawksbill turtle. Some reptiles lay more than once during a nesting season. The usual number of nestings for the green turtle is three or four, but there may be as many as seven clutches laid, at intervals of nearly two weeks. The green turtle is one of a few reptiles of various kinds known not to nest every year.

In the big snakes, there appears to be an interesting correlation between the size of the individual and the number of eggs it may lay. On the average, the majority of snake species throughout the world lays between eight and 15 eggs at a time, but big constrictors will considerably exceed this number. Among the African rock pythons, for example, a 14-foot individual will lay about 20 eggs, but a 22-foot snake produces up to 100. An 18-foot reticulate python lays about 33 eggs, whereas a 25-foot female is known to lay as many as 103 at a time.

Reptiles usually lay their eggs in sand, soil, humus or rotting logs. The nests range from an angle between tree roots or a scratch in the soil to the deep, cleanly urn-shaped cavity made by some female turtles or the mounded nest of the alligator.

Crocodilians diverge widely in nesting habits. The American crocodile digs holes in the sand as sea turtles do. The American alligator, however, searches out a place at the edge of a pond or marsh where moist debris—leaf mold, twigs and branches, and even growing shrubbery—is available. This she scrapes into a high mound, and then digs a cavity in the top of the heap, deposits her eggs in it and covers it with material from the edges of the mound. This marked difference in a fundamental behavioral process may indicate a basic long-term divergence in crocodilian ecology. Perhaps the crocodiles have, since early in their history, been riparian and marine animals, and thus still tend to nest in the sand of bars and beaches. The alligator, on the other hand, may always have been a dweller in swamps, and as such has kept the tendency to build a raised nest, and to make it of stuff most likely to be available in swamps or marshes but not on the seashore. The mounded nest site raises the eggs above the waterlogged floor of the swamp, and the decomposition of the organic nest material furnishes the heat needed for incubation which is lacking in the shaded nesting place.

O N a recent visit to the Caribbean coast between Honduras and Guatemala, I was stimulated to see on one clean stretch of salt beach the remains of nests and eggshells of three different reptiles all mixed together along the shore. One was the hawksbill sea turtle, which is fairly common in the waters of the region. The other was the American crocodile. The third was the big tree iguana, which has become thoroughly adjusted to a life that takes advantages from both arboreal and aquatic habitats. The mature iguanas spend nearly all their foraging and sleeping hours in trees overhanging the water. But if you seem to an iguana to be pressing it closely in its tree, it will simply let go and fall cleanly into the water. Under water it swims almost as well as a crocodilian, and conceals itself among roots or in cavities in the bank till the alarm is over. Different as the lives of iguanas, sea turtles and crocodiles are, the sand of the ocean beach offers the same attractions to all three animals as a place for incubating eggs.

With the end of the incubation period, the reptilian egg that has afforded such protection to the developing embryo becomes a prison to the young crea-

A MATERNAL ALLIGATOR

The female American alligator builds her nest by biting off huge mouthfuls of damp vegetable trash and combining them with mud to form a mound which may be six feet wide at its base and a yard high. From 15 to 80 eggs are then laid in a hole scooped out of the top. This is promptly covered by material pulled from the rim and packed down smooth.

Unlike most reptiles, which abandon their eggs after laying, the alligator hovers about to guard the eggs from other animals. When it is time to hatch, the baby alligators make faint squeaking sounds, signaling their mother to amble over and help them tear open the mound.

ture inside, and clearly some device is needed to enable the hatchling to break out of the tough shell and membrane into the world. This is provided in snakes and lizards in the form of the egg tooth, a true if tiny tooth carried on the premaxillary bone and used by the little reptile to cut its way free. In turtles and crocodilians a similar function is carried out by the caruncle, a horny projection on the tip of the snout. Egg teeth and caruncles are shed soon after hatching—in the lizards and snakes usually within a day or two, in some turtles and crocodilians in two to four weeks.

Breaking out of the egg is a process that may take considerable time, even with the help of an egg tooth and certain secretions which, as hatching approaches, help the reptile young to free themselves by weakening the membranes and shells. In most reptiles, it takes several hours; in some, like the larger snakes, it may take as long as several days. Some of the turtles that spend their first winter after hatching in the nest may remain in the broken shell until the following spring.

CARE for the eggs during incubation, or for the young after hatching, is not characteristic of reptiles, but a very few species do show various, in some cases surprising, degrees of instinctive parental concern. One of the pythons, for instance, appears to brood its eggs, contributing perhaps some degree of metabolic heat to them—in any case, it coils around them in a protective fashion and will even continue to coil around the empty space if the eggs are removed. Certain colubrine snakes also have the brooding habit, as does one of the viper species. Among the lizards, the so-called glass snake and some related species coil around the clutch of eggs in the same way. Some of the American skinks of the genus *Eumeces* actively tend their eggs from the time they are laid in the nest until they hatch. During incubation, these lizards will ward off intruders, turn the eggs regularly and provide brooding warmth from their own sun-warmed bodies. One species even nursemaids its brood after the hatching: it assists the young to break out of the egg, sees to it that they can feed undisturbed, and cleanses their cloacal regions with its tongue.

This sort of postnatal care is certainly the exception among reptiles; turtles, for instance, show no suggestion of brooding or parental care whatever. Nor do most crocodilians, except for the alligator, which may return often to the nest site to fuss about, reshaping and moistening it during incubation and, when the croaking of hatched young is heard inside, to help them get out of the nest mound. After the young hatch, too, the mother may retain some of her solicitude for them. Old alligators are often found in the company of bands of small ones. This may in part be simply because the hatchlings proceed directly to the nearest open water around, as likely as not a "gator hole"—a deep pool sloshed out by a big alligator as a lurking place. Nests are frequently made near such holes, or the pools are made near the nesting site where the female keeps her watch during the incubation period. In the swamps and marshes in which alligators usually nest, a gator hole near the nest would be a logical place for the young to go to when they hatch—irrespective of whether they might get any protective attention from the parent. The point is debated by alligator hunters and other experts, but my own experience leads me to think that a gator hole with mother and hatchlings in it is indeed a rude sort of nursery. Certainly a female alligator in such a place, surrounded by offspring of even as much as several weeks old, can be expected to be more irritable and resentful of intrusion than Florida alligators are at other stages of their careers. I have twice blundered into such company while wading after frogs. Both times I nearly drowned myself in fright when the old alligator suddenly rushed halfway across the hole toward me in what seemed clearly a belligerent way. While in both cases the alligators stopped too short for biting, the point is that both mothers made overt defensive moves that quickly took my mind off any plan of putting their offspring in a bag, and would probably have had a comparable effect on any potential natural enemy. A few alligator men with whom I have discussed these incidents have assured me that the alligators that rushed at me were as scared as I was and were really only dashing away in panic. Other men who appear just as versed in gator lore say this is not so, that the seeming pugnacity is real.

In any case there can be no doubt that bands of sibling alligators hold together for long periods after hatching, and that their croakings draw the mother to them. That alligators can be called out into view by a man croaking like a little one is proof of this, and I saw other evidence of it only recently when my boys found a school of young alligators with an old one in a sinkhole at the edge of a lake, and called me to look at them. These were not new hatchlings but were at least two months old. Nevertheless, they were still banded together in a loose sort of way, and when found were for some reason croaking so loudly in ragged unison that they could be heard from 50 yards off in the woods. They sounded like an uncertain chorus of some unknown frog. When we moved out onto the bank an old alligator cruised away into a patch of maiden cane. Clearly the young were hers, and clearly she still kept scraps of instinctive concern for them—she glided out of the grass and moved a few feet toward us each time the bobbing young resumed their croaking, and also each time we imitated it. There was no sign of fight in her, but her moves were not the usual flight to the far fastnesses of the lake—they were sallies in our direction. Later we caught four of the little alligators. They ranged in length from 14½ to 16 inches. This mother alligator's maternal drive had thus lasted at least two months and perhaps three. Later it may disappear completely, and she will eat as many of her offspring as she can catch.

O NE of the conspicuous features of reptilian behavior is the seasonal aggregating of some turtles at nesting sites. The life cycle of an aquatic reptile is in broad outline a reversal of that of the amphibian. Most frogs go back to water to lay their aquatic eggs. Most water reptiles go to the shore to lay theirs. In some cases any kind of shore may be suitable, and the females thus are likely to emerge singly. But some turtles make long journeys to congregate at a specially favored shore or in a few miles of preferred beach. The most massive known reproductive aggregations of any fresh-water reptile are those of a side-necked turtle, the arrau (*Podocnemis*) of the Orinoco and Amazon Rivers. Since the early naturalists explored the Amazon and Orinoco, the nesting assemblages of *Podocnemis* on certain sandy islands in the rivers has been a theme for excited reporting. The turtles come to the chosen islands from great distances up and down the river, and the gatherings are so vast that actual overcrowding of the nesting bars sometimes occurs. The adaptive function of the migration is not wholly clear. In part it may be dictated by the need for a special set of nesting conditions; but to some extent it may also be simply a hereditary tendency to cling to ancestral travel habits. In any case, the resulting aggregations are spectacular, and the people of the regions have, since pre-Columbian times, depended heavily on the nesting colonies for meat and eggs.

THE WIDE-RANGING GREEN TURTLE

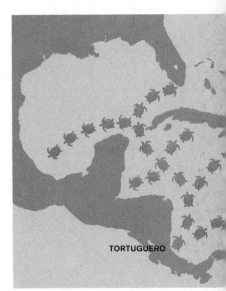

TORTUGUERO

Although green turtles may roam as far as 1,200 miles between their nesting site and foraging grounds in the Caribbean, their travel routes remain in the realm of the unknown. The map above indicates their presumed paths, based on a tagging program initiated in 1955 at Tortuguero, Costa Rica, in which 3,000 adult female turtles were marked. Of these, 108 were later picked up at sites indicated by the turtles at the end of each row on the map. Those drawn between Tortuguero and the recovery sites show probable travel paths.

All sea turtles appear to be migratory, and at least part of the periodic travel of all the species is back and forth between foraging places and nesting grounds. From information now available the hawksbill seems the least inclined to gather in groups for nesting, but even in that species some reproduction is weakly colonial and some carried out by widely spaced individuals.

The most clear-cut nesting migrations are those of the green turtle. Since this creature is herbivorous, most of its adult life is spent foraging on submarine pastures of marine plants. These may lie at considerable distance from the nesting beach. A favored nesting shore thus recruits turtles from different areas, and some of these may lie many hundreds of miles away. The green turtles of the coast of Brazil migrate 1,400 miles to Ascension Island, a dot in the middle of the South Atlantic, battling contrary currents, and staying on course by signs and senses not yet understood.

IN some ways the most dramatic of all marine reptile activities, and among the most impressive assemblages of any aquatic animal are the *arribadas*, or arrivals, of the Atlantic ridley, a short-shelled, big-headed sea turtle whose breeding habits were until lately almost wholly unknown. Ridleys foregather in immense assemblages on the northern gulf coast of Mexico. Henry Hildebrand of the University of Corpus Christi has described them in a recent paper. One of these incredible aggregations was filmed by Señor Andres Herrera of Tampico, Mexico, in 1948, and his film lay unnoticed by zoologists until discovered by Doctor Hildebrand and shown at the Austin, Texas, meetings of the American Society of Ichthyologists and Herpetologists.

Señor Herrera generously let me have a copy of his film. I have studied it repeatedly, and it seems to me one of the most dramatic revelations of modern zoology. In the first place the film was made in the daytime, whereas most sea turtles nest at night. Señor Herrera and Doctor Hildebrand estimate that 10,000 ridleys are in view in the mile of beach shown, and that at least 40,000 were there during the whole day of the *arribada*. The film gives the impression that one could walk away into the distance for miles, stepping from the back of one nesting ridley to another. The arrivals occur at wholly unpredictable times from April through June. The time signal may vary from year to year, but all the turtles get it and swarm ashore, along many miles of almost uninhabited beach line. There are said to be three *arribadas* a year, and they occur at different points on the beach. This is a good thing because the sand of a section already visited must surely be loaded with eggs, and a renesting at the same site could only destroy much of the result of the one that preceded it.

Some of the sea snakes periodically band together in the ocean, presumably for reproductive purposes. There is an old report of a migrating train of sea snakes 60 miles long, and several species have been seen in smaller conclaves. Most sea snakes are live-bearing animals, and thus do not come together for nesting. The gatherings therefore are simply a means of mobilizing the sexes at mating time. Much probably remains to be learned of the social customs of sea snakes.

In fact, much remains to be learned about the whole subject of reptile reproduction. The great innovation reptiles made, putting a shell on their egg, seems a forthright, even simple evolutionary move. But the adjustments this single advance brought on have gone spreading and weaving through the lives of all of us for 300 million years. The songs of birds are because of the egg with a shell, and so are the thoughts of men.

BREAKING FROM ITS EGG, A 10-INCH BABY CROCODILE MAKES AN AWKWARD ENTRY AT LONDON'S ZOO. AS AN ADULT IT MAY REACH 16 FEET

Courtship and Egg-Laying

As the first vertebrates to venture far from water into the continental heartlands, reptiles had to evolve hardy eggs and the advanced mating practices that go with life on land. The hardiness of their eggs is confirmed by the one above, which was laid in Africa but hatched in London. Some of the odd ceremonials connected with reptile reproduction are depicted on the following pages.

TEST BY WRESTLING between two red diamondback rattlers *(above)* starts out with one climbing up the other. When they overreach and collapse inconclusively *(below)*, they writhe and spar in preparation for the next fall.

Combat and Color among the Males

The generally accepted practice in the animal kingdom, when the time comes to reproduce the species, is for the males to put on a show that will impress and captivate the females—a courting activity which extends right up to man. As in other matters, however, reptiles have their own ways of doing things: their efforts at courtship time, while still confined to the males, seem to be directed more at discouraging male rivals than at winning over females.

The show the males put on is impressive. Some may engage in ritualistic combat, like the two diamondback rattlers shown at left, wrestling gracefully and sinuously to repeated falls. Others, like the anole lizard opposite, put on gaudy colors and spread frightening fans to intimidate rivals. Some lizards dance, others affect strange, stiff-legged gaits. The net effect is to single out the fittest members of the male population as breeders, leaving the weaker to go elsewhere—a useful practice that may date back to earliest reptile times. As for the females, though they seem generally oblivious to these exaggerated male antics, they succumb in the end and mating takes place.

TEST BY INTIMIDATION is practiced by the male anole lizard, which can spread these flaccid folds beneath its chin to a fan of bright color at mating time. A cartilage rod inside serves to flare out the lavender skin.

THE FRUITS OF LABOR, three large eggs, lie beside an indigo snake as she lays a fourth one. Here photographed in captivity, she would normally lay her clutch in a burrow underground.

The Mother and Her Eggs

The end product of reptilian mating represents one of the great triumphs of evolution: an egg that comes into the world fertilized and fortified, externally by a shell, internally with food and water for the entire development of the embryo inside it. Such an egg has a pretty good chance of surviving on its own, and indeed, there are few reptile eggs that get any maternal attention at all throughout the period of incubation. Turtles, who lay the most eggs—up

TWO LARGE WHITE EGGS OF A TEMPORARILY TAILLESS TURKISH GECKO SHINE THROUGH THE TRANSLUCENT SKIN OF HER BELLY. SOON SHE WI▶

to 400 a year in the case of sea turtles—care for them the least, generally abandoning them to the sand or earth in which they bury them. Crocodiles, lizards and snakes normally lay fewer eggs, but may do more for them—exploiting the sun to keep them warm, or supplementing sunlight with the warmth generated by decay in nests of rotting vegetation. Still others guard their eggs against predators, and one, the Indian python, broods them like a hen.

THE BURIED NEST of a peninsula cooter, a Florida fresh-water turtle, shows a clutch of eggs buried deeply, with two left at the sides, possibly as decoys to mislead nest-robbing predators.

AY THEM, UNDER A STONE OR OTHER SHELTER, TO HATCH IN A FEW MONTHS AND GROW, LIKE THEIR MOTHER, INTO AMIABLE HOUSE PROWLERS

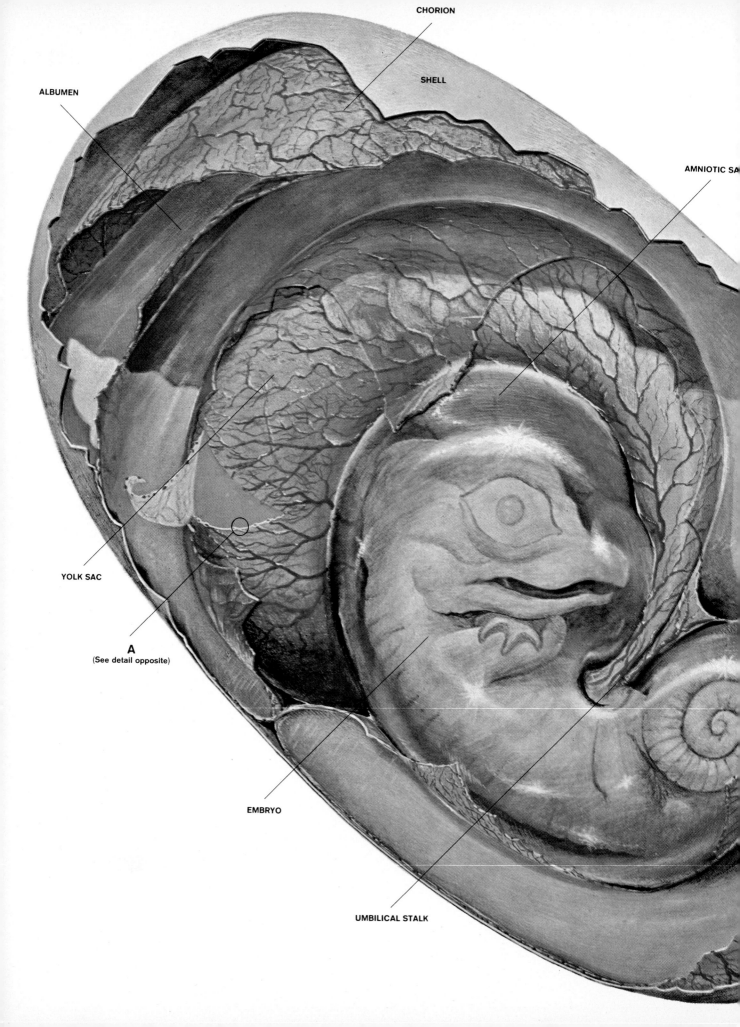

ALBUMEN

CHORION

SHELL

AMNIOTIC SA

YOLK SAC

A
(See detail opposite)

EMBRYO

UMBILICAL STALK

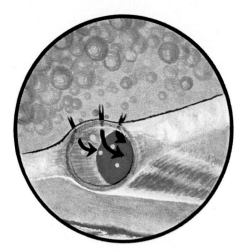

HOW THE EMBRYO FEEDS

Food conduits in the form of blood vessels in the lining of the egg's yolk sac (circled area A, opposite) take up nutritious chemicals from the rich golden store of sugars, starches, fats and proteins laid away in the yolk. The blood proceeds to circulate them throughout the whole yolk wall. Thus they reach the abdominal region of the embryo where they are in turn used for growth. Waste chemicals pass out of the embryo into the fluid of the allantois.

HOW THE EMBRYO BREATHES

Gas vents in the porous shell wall (circled area B, left) are revealed as small holes in the enlargement at right. These let life-giving oxygen into the alligator egg and poisonous carbon dioxide out of it. The oxygen is captured by oxygen-hungry hemoglobin molecules in the blood vessels of the chorion, which carry the vital gas by way of the allantois to the embryo. The carbon dioxide escapes from the blood by a process of seepage known as gaseous diffusion.

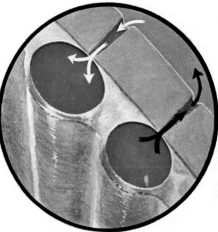

ALLANTOIS

B
(See detail at right)

Inside the Egg

Compared to the simple eggs of fishes and amphibians, which are laid in water and often depend on it to bring fertilizing sperm to them, the reptile egg is a staggering innovation—the product of eons of development which started when the reptiles' amphibian ancestors first took up internal fertilization. The alligator egg at left, with its embryo in a halfway stage of development, typifies the complexity of most reptile eggs. The embryo in the center is connected by an umbilical stalk to the primary food supply, the yellow yolk sac, and is encased in the amniotic sac, an envelope filled with fluid which laves the embryo and cushions it from shock. The amniotic sac and yolk sac, in turn, are surrounded by still another envelope, the allantois, which in the early stages of development grows out from the embryo's hind-gut. The allantois gets larger as the embryo grows and the yolk shrinks. It serves both as a storage bladder for uric acid, ammonia and other wastes, and as a conveyor for incoming oxygen and outgoing carbon dioxide. Another membrane, the chorion, encloses allantois, amniotic sac, yolk sac and embryo in a tough, resilient envelope closely associated with the eggshell itself. In crocodilians and turtles, the chorion contains egg white, or albumen, which serves to supply the embryo with water and probably some food.

TINY OFFSPRING OF AN AMERICAN RED-BELLIED SNAKE, BORN ALIVE BUT SO SMALL THAT THEY CAN COIL ON DIMES, WRIGGLE ALL OVER THE

HATCHLINGS of the common snapping turtle are barely an inch long. When grown they will weigh 30 pounds apiece, but they are belligerent from the start, always ready with a quick nip.

The Hazards of Hatching

The protection which the shelled egg gives to the developing embryo is its most obvious contribution to the survival of the species—but scarcely less important is the fact that when it hatches, it lets out into the world a tiny miniature of an adult, equipped from the beginning to make its own way in its environment. But to reach this perfected state the embryo needs a long period of development in the egg. Turtles like the snappers at left need two to three months; the primitive but specialized New Zealand tuatara needs more than a year. During these long incubations the eggs must be protected from predators and other dangers. Turtles get around this by

10-INCH MOTHER. SMALL AS THEY ARE, THESE YOUNG ALREADY HAVE THE HUNTING INSTINCT AND FEED THEMSELVES ON SLUGS AND EARTHWORMS

laying scores of eggs and burying them for concealment in sand or earth. Tuataras' eggs, which are
buried in shallow holes near their burrows, are given
still further protection by the very remoteness and
desolation of their island hatcheries. But many reptiles have evolved ways of keeping their eggs during
part or even all of their incubation period in the
safest of all hiding places: the body of the mother.
Some hatch the eggs in the oviduct, some have developed placentalike connections, similar to those in
mammals, to feed the embryo as it grows. But however they are born, baby reptiles meet the world
fully formed and prepared to fend for themselves.

COPPERHEAD FRY, roughly nine inches long, are born in sacs,
the last relics of egghood. In half an hour, already poisonous
enough to kill small prey, they will break from these sheaths.

143

Cutting Out to Meet the World

How tentative and experimental the reptiles still are in their efforts to abandon the egg and bear their young alive is dramatically demonstrated by a special little tool which all of them, even the live-born, still have. This is the egg tooth, a sharp protrusion on the snout with which a baby reptile can cut its way out of its tough, membrane-lined shell. To be sure, in live-bearing species which have no need for it the egg tooth is degenerating (even the egg-layers drop it soon after birth). But it still stands as a reminder of the difficult escape problem the shelled egg has always presented for the beakless reptiles.

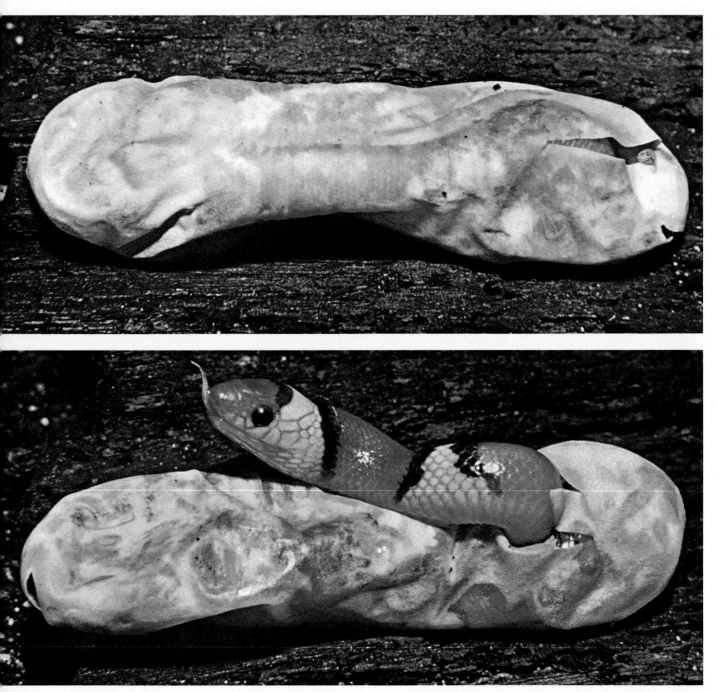

CUTTING ITS WAY into the world, a baby scarlet snake makes the first slit in the egg's shell *(top picture)*. Several hours later, it has enlarged the hole sufficiently to crawl out, fully formed.

CLOSE-UP of the baby snake's head *(opposite)* at the moment of emergence from the shell shows the egg tooth as a tiny triangle at the top of the picture just left of where the mouth begins.

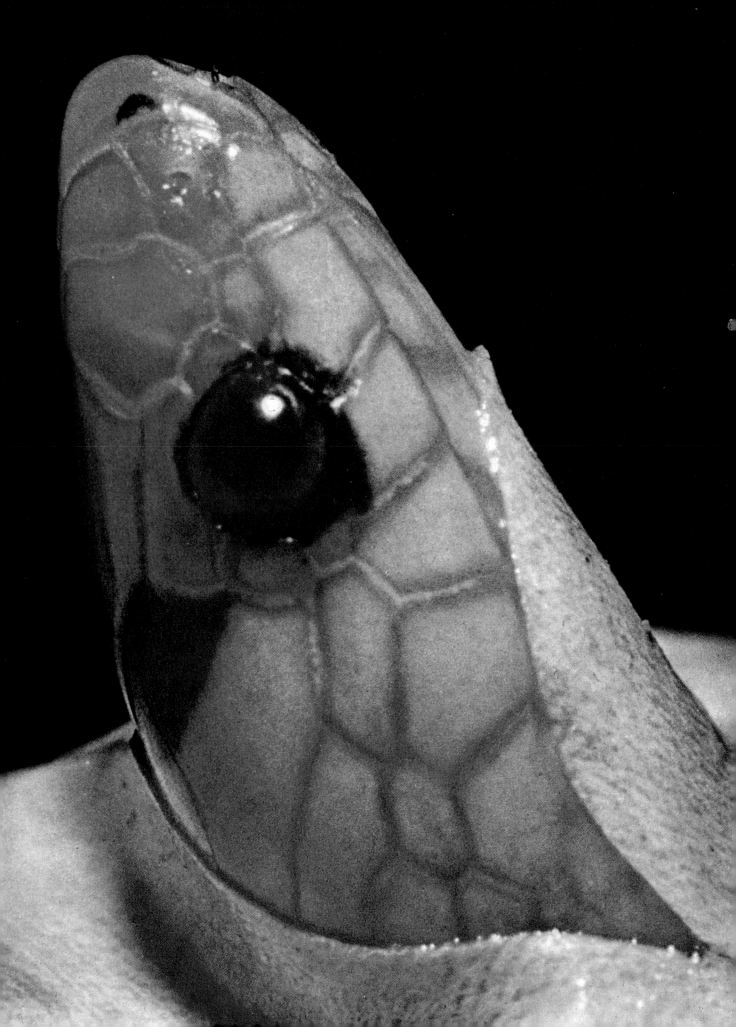

I suppose the chance was just too good for St. Patrick's public relations men to miss. I believe it is not generally known that someone once fetched a lot of snakes into Ireland in an effort to establish them there. I cannot say whether this was done idly or scientifically or in a spirit of iconoclasm. The *Edinburgh New Philosophical Journal* for April 1835 had only this to say of the event:

"We have learned from good authority that a recent importation of snakes has been made into Ireland, and that at present they are multiplying rapidly within a few miles of St. Patrick's tomb."

Both turtles and snakes turn up repeatedly in Asiatic mythology. The third incarnation of Vishnu, the supreme god in the Hindu pantheon, was in the form of a turtle. At Vishnu's suggestion the gods and demons set out to churn the ocean of milk to bring up the amrita, the liquor of immortality. They uprooted Mount Meru and set it in the sea as a churn staff. They somehow persuaded the great snake Vasuki to throw a half-hitch of his body around the staff and to let himself be used as a churn rope. Vishnu took the form of a big sea turtle and placed himself under the foot of the staff as a pivot base. There was some squabbling among gods and demons as to which would pull the head end of the churn rope and which the ignoble afterend, but after a while they all fell to and churned for a thousand years. At one point the snake grew indisposed and threw up a terrible poison that came close to killing off all the gods, but Siva seized and swallowed it, and that is how his throat came to be blue. After other awesome vicissitudes the goblet of amrita finally came up, and likewise the comely Lakshmi, the goddess of beauty.

Another set of reptilian beings important in Indian mythology was a fabulous race of snakes, or half-snakes, often shown as put together of a human forepart with the back part normal snake. The males of these were called Nagas and their wives Naginas; and their natures were generally irresponsible and ornery. On the other hand, some Hindu snakes were beneficent. During the epochs of his cosmic rest—the times between his incarnations—Vishnu sleeps on the coils of the noble cobra Shesha, whose seven heads rise over the god as shade for his eon-long siesta. This is why Indians are kind to cobras.

ALL over the warm parts of the earth, crocodilians have been taken into religion and mythology. In many places the veneration is a sort of bribery, in which crocodiles are fed to gain their good will. Other cults carefully kill only crocodiles that have attacked people. At Lake Itasy in Madagascar a yearly proclamation is made announcing formally to the crocodiles that the evil ones among them—those which have killed someone during the past year—will be liquidated in their turn, and that all upright crocodiles should thus stay out of the way. In ancient Egypt, crocodiles were worshiped. Herodotus said that in parts of Egypt each household had a tame crocodile, which was fed daily, adorned with jewels and, when it died, embalmed and placed in a sacred repository. Crocodile mummies have been found in tombs. Crocodiles are still kept by fakirs near Karachi in Pakistan, and devout pilgrims buy goats which are cut up and fed to them.

All up and down the Americas reptiles were involved in the religions of the Indians in various ways. The most influential American reptile god—in this case a half-reptile god—was Quetzalcoatl, the feathered serpent and the "fair god" of the ancient Mexicans. This deity was put together from two stirring animals of the Mexican world: the quetzal and the rattlesnake. The quetzal is the resplendent trogon, the most striking of American birds. To this day, seeing a quetzal slash through the green gloom of the cloud forest will make a mystic of the average man. The rattlesnake, especially the big diamondback and irascible tropical rattlesnake that the Toltecs and Aztecs knew, is one of the more imposing reptiles anywhere. The quetzal came to mean the wind, and the rattlesnake the whirlwind; put together they were Quetzalcoatl, who pushed the clouds.

Pushing clouds brought on rain, and so put fertility into the land, and from there all blessings flowed. Like most primitive gods, Quetzalcoatl had such varied manifestations that it takes a specialist to trace them out. One of his exploits was sailing forth across the Gulf of Mexico on a raft of serpents. When the Spaniards landed in Mexico, the emperor Montezuma thought they were Quetzalcoatl and his retinue returning, and this weakened his resistance to the invasion and hastened the fall of the Aztec Empire. The feathered serpent was prevalent in pre-Columbian architecture and decoration through most of southern Mexico, Yucatan and Guatemala. I had lived in the Honduras mountains for three years when archeologist Doris Stone came by one day excited over a rumor of "painted rocks," and we rode to the far side of my favorite mountain and found Quetzalcoatl there, engraved in the rhyolite face of a shallow scarp.

SINCE the dimmest of ancient times Europeans have been religious about vipers. Pliny and Galen prescribed the eating of vipers as a cure for various ills. Both viper broth and the boiled flesh, either prepared at home or bought at the apothecary's, were popular remedies until fairly recent times. Among the ancient Gauls the magic spread from the adder itself to a potent charm called *glein neidr*—serpent's egg, or adder stone. These adder stones were actually old beads found about the countryside, but the Druids claimed that they were produced by a group reproductive effort of a summer congress of adders, and held some of the magic of the parent snakes. Adder stones strengthened their owners in legal disputes and helped them get access to kings. In Celtic parts of the United Kingdom the beads were until recent decades still valued by country people for driving away an ague or protecting children from such childhood ailments as whooping cough. Perhaps they still are.

In eastern Europe and the Middle East a cult persisted until recently in which snakes were made welcome in farmhouses and allowed to live there rather like beneficent spirits—perhaps a leftover from the Greek and Roman custom of keeping snakes to hold down the rat and mouse population. When the cry of the house adder was heard in the evening (needless to say no adder can cry, but that is quibbling) a saucer of milk, covered half over by a clean white cloth, was put out for it, and the adder would come and drink. At least the milk would sometimes be gone the next morning. Whether it ever disappeared in houses in which there was no dog or cat I have never heard. In various parts of Africa house snakes are offered milk too, although there the snakes are thought to be relatives come back in serpent form. I do not suppose there could be any ethnic kinship in the two cults, but all the same it is curious that milk should be the propitiatory offering in both cases, because snakes do not like milk. At least none of mine ever did. And I have tried a lot of snakes on milk, to see whether there could be any sense at all in the various milk-snake stories you hear in the Americas. One of the best-known folk beliefs about snakes in the United States is that a kind of king snake steals milk straight from the udder of the cow. As fastidious as cows are about both snakes and strange sensations in their udders, the myth is not worth much thought, except for the coincidence of its dealing with milk again. But this even makes one recall that in the Hindu legend it was a snake that was used as a spindle rope to churn the ocean of milk. Even though all these

MYTHICAL REPTILES

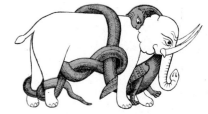

Medieval men entertained some bizarre notions about reptiles. Draco the Dragon was described in a 12th Century bestiary as the biggest of all living things. The strength of this serpentlike beast was supposed to lie not in its teeth, but in a long coiled tail that could suffocate an elephant (above). Beyond these fancies, its genesis remains obscure, but the Crocodylus (below) clearly derives from the African crocodile. It was named for its "crocus" color. Bred in the Nile, it was correctly assumed to be active at night, to incubate its eggs in the earth, and to eat people. However, its long legs, clawed feet, prominent ears and tail are imaginary.

coincidences are probably fortuitous, they serve to show the close, graded relationship between religion and folklore generally. The folklore of reptiles is immensely rich and would make a book in itself.

Even where snakes are not objects of worship or deification, their mystic influence on the human mind shows up in the many-faced phenomenon of snake-charming. As a model for this form of psychopathology, I find it helpful to look back to my own extreme youth in the days of the first World War. There was a streetcar stop near our house, where doughboys from three big training camps came and went. It was the mode of the day to "do one's bit," and in accordance with this I used to get a bag of garter snakes and take it to the car stop, and move from one soldier to another offering him a snake. Purportedly I was helping build morale by supplying the military with mascots. What I was really doing, though, I see clearly now, was making occasion to savor the stir when I thrust my hand into a bag of snakes and pulled one out with utter insouciance, and heard the soldiers say, "Come here, Bill—look what this kid's got." For that little time I was a shaman, an Appalachian preacher waving a fiery serpent before an ecstatic congregation, a carnival lady draped about a vat of brainwashed pythons, a Hopi of the Antelope or Snake priesthoods stamping around with a live rattlesnake squirming in my teeth. Like Dr. Freud finding his own libido before any other, I can say now that I was not motivated to help the war effort at all. I was only getting for myself a moment of grandeur out of our old emotional entanglement with serpents.

THE best snake charmers have always lived in the East. Some of the things they do are not yet wholly understood. Although through the centuries Indian snake charmers have been given a great deal of critical attention by visitors determined to be objective and "bring out the true facts," I know of no really adequate appraisal of the art. In some cases the snakes involved were found to have had their fangs drawn or their mouths sewn shut, but obviously such tactics are not the whole answer, because in most cases they are unharmed and perfectly capable of biting. In fact, there was a case a few years ago of a lady snake charmer in Baltimore who was bitten by one of her cobras and died. In any case, the snake charmers of India are said to have to swear a holy oath that they will keep a snake only six months, so that they are constantly having to renew their stock, on pain of being bitten if they violate their promise.

So the question really is whether the snakes are simply tame, or whether the charmer knows tricks of snake psychology unknown to other men. Clifford Pope thinks the charmed snakes may just be disarmed by being well fed and compares the charmed snake to one basking in the sun, similarly lethargic and not to be frightened away by talking or even shouting. Certainly it is not the music that does whatever charming may be done. Pope records an experiment in which snakes were subjected to terrific noises. Their eyes were taped and then bugles were blown and large tin cans were beaten near their heads. The snakes, being deaf, showed no reaction whatsoever. They did, however, react immediately when anyone walked or moved a chair nearby—such movements being transmitted as vibrations through the ground. The belief, however, that music charms snakes dies hard.

Snake-charming is a practice ancient enough to be mentioned in the Bible, and it came to the New World too, bringing rattlesnakes into its lore and legend. There is a story, for instance, mentioned by Laurence M. Klauber in his monumental work on rattlesnakes, of a berry picker who used a mouth organ to render rattlers harmless while he went about his work and another very tall tale of an Indian who trained a band of rattlesnakes to join him in a mixed chorus: the snakes, which ranged from small to large, carried the soprano, alto, tenor and bass parts with their rattles.

Apart from music, however, one thing all snake charmers, whether in India or among the Hopi Indians, have in common is rhythmic and incessant movements of their arms, bodies and, in snake dances, of their legs. It is possible that snakes may be bewildered by this, possibly even hypnotized in some way. But in any case, with or without a mystic rapport between snake and man, snake-charming recalls an old mindless horror in a small pageant of man, snake, flute and basket; and the pageant plays on primate juices for about the same reasons that a Spanish bullfight does. A good snake charmer gives a good show. It is a great shame that crude charlatans fake so stupidly, or go overboard with revolting zeal, as in the case reported by a traveler in Egypt, and quoted by the *Pictorial Museum of Animated Nature:*

"I have seen at Cairo a man who came from above the Catacombs, where the pits of the mummy-birds are, who has taken a cerastes [a horned viper] with his naked hand from a number of others at the bottom of a tub, put it upon his bare head, and tied it about his neck like a necklace. After which it has been applied to a hen, and bit it, which has died in a few minutes: and to complete the experiment, the man has taken it by the neck, and beginning at the tail has eaten it as one would do a carrot or stock of celery, without any seeming repugnance."

Being both pictorial and endowed with a background of mysticism, reptiles have served in all kinds of ways as symbols in heraldry. The turtle stands for invulnerability to attack; the reptilelike dragon for aggressive invincibility, showing up as a fierce symbol on shields and banners all around the world and all through history. The Manchu emperors used it, and so did the Mikado, and so do the British, who incorporated it in the royal arms when they incorporated Wales. The basilisk of fable is a sort of snake-lizard whose very glance is fatal— hence the deadly qualities of literature's "basilisk stare." The basilisk probably derives from the royal cobra of ancient Egypt. Its nominal modern representative is a genus of tropical American lizards, *Basiliscus*, which flaunt erectile crests along their heads and backs in a frightening fashion.

IN American heraldry, not surprisingly, it is the rattlesnake that plays the major role. DONT TREAD ON ME was the warning motto of the coiled rattler pictured on the banner of John Proctor's Independent Battalion of Westmoreland County when these Pennsylvanians went to war against the British, and the first Navy Jack carried a rattler out onto the high seas, stretched diagonally from lower right to upper left across the 13 red and white stripes symbolizing the colonies. One of the original companies of the Marines also had a rattlesnake painted on its drum when that newly formed corps first saw action.

Another and usually more peaceful way in which reptiles and people are involved with each other is in the keeping of reptiles as pets. Little boys have always liked any reptile they were not afraid of or, if the liking was affected, the wonderful reaction the reptiles produced in girls certainly was not. But until lately, when a pet was taken into the bosom of a family it was generally furred or feathered, and hardly ever was a scaly reptile. Now however, at first in Europe and a bit more slowly in the United States, reptiles are being taken increasingly into households; and this time it is not as ancestors snooping about in reptile form, but as agreeable and rewarding animal companions. Not long ago little

HOW TO HANDLE
REPTILIAN PETS

A small lizard can be held by pressing the thumb gently on a hind leg. Grabbing it by the tip of its tail may break it off.

Grasping a snake's neck carefully behind the head will keep it from biting. Squeezing too tightly will increase its struggles.

Crocodilians may be held in the manner shown above. Reptiles should not be disturbed for an hour or two after eating.

turtles, anole chameleons and baby alligators were almost the only reptiles to be found for sale in American pet stores. Today, in many cities you can choose from a varied line of lizards, snakes and turtles in the pet shops, and this commerce has suddenly become one of the principal ways in which man is exploiting reptiles to his material gain. By far the most popular reptilian pets are baby turtles, which are hatched for the trade by millions in Mississippi Valley hatcheries. The sale of baby alligators is now prohibited, but importation of tropical caimans is filling the gap. Snakes and lizards, because they are partial to live food, are a little less easy to keep than turtles, but for a determined culturist this is no real problem. People are keeping snakes and lizards all about the land, and are no doubt better people for it.

It is perhaps idle but nonetheless engaging to speculate about the origins of the odd spiritual ties between reptiles and man. The new vogue for reptile pets, like the little boys' old interest in them, is part bravado—a swelling pride in shedding a fear. Therefore, the origin of the conquered fear is the thing that seems worth psychological attention. Some of it is traditional, learned or affected. Part of it, however, may be innate. For a long time it has been the habit of sages to deride the popular belief that the dread of snakes is instinctive. They point out that a baby does not recoil at a proffered snake; he accepts and chews on it joyously. But this means nothing. The same baby will not whistle when a pretty girl passes. The anthropoid animal has had long evolutionary communion with serpents. There is growing evidence that a main center of human evolution was in a part of Africa where cobras, mambas and pythons are common today and have likely been for a long time. It is unthinkable that with such a background we should have failed to acquire any inherent snake-avoidance adaptations. It is even less likely that we should have wholly lost them.

That is to say, I am pretty sure a little of the fear of snakes *is* instinctive. The greater part of it no doubt comes from the harrowing way Grandma took on over the whiteoak snake in the privy—from being marked by hearing the tale in the third and fourth generation. But to say without proof that any ape has got over all its hereditary readiness for the snake crisis makes little sense. Your dog goes around and around before lying down in the long-dead grass of your living-room rug—and your mind goes around at the sudden sight of a snake.

THE lot of reptiles, living on earth with man these latter years, is mainly decimation. By an odd eddy in the current of progress, however, some things we do turn out to further the reptile cause. For instance, land reptiles eat whole small animals, and man does a number of things that favor the increase of these. Predator control is one such thing. Quail management in south Georgia has killed off old enemies of rabbits, and the diamondback rattlesnake has now become more plentiful there than anywhere else. Cutover lands generally make better snake and lizard country than original forest, and the borders between woods and fields are also highly productive of reptiles. The gravitation of some kinds of snakes and lizards into and around human abodes was spoken of in another chapter, as was the inadvertent extension of reptile ranges by transportation in the cargoes of commerce.

Besides these more-or-less accidental aids to reptiles, man has erected a few preserves to save threatened species. The islands set aside for the tuatara in New Zealand are the most notable example. The desert tortoise is protected in California, the diamondback terrapin on part of the Atlantic Coast and the Gila monster and horned lizard in Arizona. For a time there was a python preserve in

Lake Chilwa in Nyasaland. In most of the national parks and wildlife sanctuaries of the world reptiles are more or less shielded from persecution. The American alligator gets varyingly effective protection in Florida, Georgia and Alabama, although in Mississippi it gets none at all. In the opinion of people who have carefully appraised the position of crocodilians in the modern world, they are now clearly in danger of disappearing, species by species, before the spread of human culture. There can be no doubt whatever that a brief relaxation of protection for the American alligator would bring its quick and complete extinction, and other species are in a comparably insecure position.

Aᴛ this stage in history, reptiles are not a major menace to human life. The most important reptilian causes of injury and death are poisonous snakes and crocodiles. In the Indian subcontinent, where people live cosily with cobras and kraits, there are some thousands of deaths by snake bite every year. Although hard figures for the South American continent are not available, snake bite is common in some areas, and despite the pioneering in serum therapy by a Brazilian laboratory, the Butantan Institute, fatalities are frequent in the back country of the American tropics. A number of the bigger crocodilians are perversely unable to see the special nature of the human animal, and absent-mindedly eat him from time to time. One of the caimans is bad this way, and so is the salt-water crocodile of Asia. The worst is no doubt the classic Nile crocodile, chiefly because of an almost ritual indifference on the part of women who wash clothes along East African lakes and rivers. They not only wash there, under the rapt gaze of cruising crocodiles, but actually face the peril rear-end-to, clinging stubbornly to the ancestral custom of standing in the water and scrubbing the wash on a rock on the bank. It is folly to think a crocodile would ignore such an invitation; and they often do not. I am speaking mainly of villages in the southern part of the Great Rift Valley, on Lake Nyasa, or along the Shire River.

To me it is a mark of curious forbearance on the part of crocodilians that in the rest of their range they eat so few people. In Florida, for instance, where the alligator reaches sizes and appetites big enough to encompass the largest men, there is not a single record of fatal attack. The only attacks of any kind—Ross Allen of Silver Springs, Florida, has collected six authenticated cases—have involved alligators psychopathically overconfident from long association with man. Allen is scared of his own tame bull alligators, but he cheerfully swims after and manhandles the wild ones.

In the mutual feeding relationship between men and reptiles, many more reptiles than men are eaten. As reptile food, man is nowadays not a significant item. If you lie nine days unfound on the bottom of a pond the little stinkjims may finally pick at you in a desultory way. But for a man with his wits about him, being eaten by reptiles is, in much of the world, not a thing to worry about. Similarly, the majority of civilized men do not depend heavily on reptiles as food; although in one place or another about the earth natural man has always eaten reptiles of every kind.

Though turtles are generally considered the most edible of the reptiles, all kinds can be eaten and, as I said, all kinds are. The crocodilians appear on tables in various parts of their range. Crocodile meat is coarse, however, and to me confusingly intermediate in quality between fish and beef. I have never heard an enthusiastic appraisal of alligator steak by anyone not either very hungry or trying hard to be open-minded. Most of the bigger lizards are hunted for food by indigenous folk, and at least one—the big tree iguana—is very toothsome

Turtles that have long sturdy tails like the snapping turtle (above) can be picked up with a firm grasp of the tail, though prolonged handling in this way may injure them. But species with shorter tails, like the soft-shelled turtle shown below, are best handled by holding on to the back part of the upper shell. Although no turtle is venomous, many can inflict painful bites.

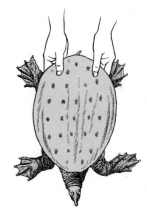

game. On the Central American coast the Creoles cook a female iguana with her unlaid eggs in a way to make you cry with joy.

Western victualers generally eschew snakes, but from early times they have been eaten by simple people. And the Japanese, whose culture is ancient and cuisine respectable, consume sea snakes in volumes that support major fisheries. Snakeries? To delicate-natured western people snakes are simply outside the pale, and the reasons for this are not clear. There is nothing offensive about snake meat—it has no alarming taste or texture. It is as good as veal cutlets. Like them, it is pallid and without force, but harmless as mother's milk and nourishing withal. Snakes look like worms in a way, and this is cited by many as grounds for their revulsion. But what is so bad about worms? And anyway, snakes are not much like them, really. There is more than worms behind the prejudice, just as the worldwide cringing of people before a harmless small snake, whether on a jungle trail or at 42nd and Broadway, is a sign of something more than worms.

IGUANA STEW

Catch a fat female iguana, preferably in March or April, kill it and skin it and remove the insides. Save the eggs, including the yellow ones, also the liver and heart. Dismember the body by cutting it down the backbone and dividing the sections in three parts and the legs in two. Place the pieces in a pot containing a little heated coconut oil and brown lightly over a low fire. Pour in enough water to cover the meat, and drop in a chile piquante and garlic to taste.

Meanwhile, in another pot of very salty water, boil the eggs in shells with a chile pod for half an hour. Drain them and add, shells and all, to the meat, along with the diced liver and heart and the yellow eggs. Now cook everything until the liquid has almost disappeared. Pour the remaining broth over red beans and rice, and heap the stewed meat on top.

OF all the reptiles it is the turtles that most notably have counted in human diets, both civilized and savage. Most primitive people living where turtles live eat them, and excavations show that this has always been so. Although in much of the western world turtle is today unknown as food, or has become a luxury or novelty item, there are in some places folk to whom it remains a staple. Sea turtles or their eggs are eaten almost wherever they can be found. In the rivers of northeastern South America turtles are a more important source of meat than any domesticated animal. In the lower Amazon the array of turtle dishes prepared involves a variety of species and almost constitutes a special endemic turtle cuisine. In China and Japan soft-shelled turtles are held in great, and I might say, wholly deserved, esteem; and the same genus has a few centers of popularity in the generally reptile-shy United States.

The big herbivorous giant tortoises have in the past been an important staple for the crews of ships on long voyages in the eastern Pacific and Indian Oceans. The statistics of the depredations of whaling vessels stopping at the Galápagos Islands during the 19th Century to take on giant tortoises are almost beyond belief. In the southeastern United States the gopher tortoise was a blessing to Indians and pioneers, and has remained so even to a few modern folk of advanced gastronomic criteria. In another chapter I mentioned the importance of the South American arrau (*Podocnemis expansa*) to people of the Amazon and Orinoco where these turtles congregate by thousands to nest on a few islands in the rivers. The naturalist H. W. Bates wrote that during the time of his South American explorations 48 million eggs of the arrau were being harvested each year at the islands.

A curious bit of ethnozoology was the culinary prestige of the salt-marsh terrapin (*Malaclemys terrapin*) in the United States during the three decades before the first World War. The terrapin somehow became a sort of gastronomic status symbol, and before Prohibition and the war shut down high living for a time, female terrapins seven and eight inches long were bringing as much as $90 a dozen. This reverence was in part justified; terrapin Maryland is a gorgeous dish. But mainly the glamor was ritual, and most of the fancy folk demanding terrapin would have done as well on gopher. Today there is more trade in freshwater snapping turtles and in the soft-shelled variety, both keenly sought by an oddly localized clientele. Philadelphia is of course the original home of snapping-turtle soup, but both snappers and soft-shelled turtles reach their economic and gastronomic peak today in St. Louis and farther north in some Wisconsin cities.

The most important source of human food among reptiles is the green sea turtle. Although clear green turtle soup is a widely revered gourmet's dish, the meat of the green turtle has not gained great popularity away from the coast. This is partly because inland cooks throw away, or never see, the best parts— the flippers, chine, calipee and calipash (the last three being, respectively, the shell edge, and the cartilaginous space-filler in the lower and upper shells, which furnish the incomparable gelatinous texture of turtle dishes). They also abuse the lean meat in ways that make it taste like veal. Both veal and lean turtle are easily mummified in cooking, and both require seasoning. The widespread breaded veal cutlet of American restaurants has one virtue, as I see it—or perhaps two: it will sustain life for an unhappy time, and it is harmless to take. It tastes just as I have always imagined human flesh must taste—though I may be unjustly maligning human flesh. Veal, I repeat, is melancholy stuff unless handled with care and skill; and it is the same to a lesser degree with lean turtle—meager turtle, my Creole friend Sibella calls it—especially when it has been frozen badly or cooked by an inland housewife. I am personally rather glad that this is so.

Two recent trends are dimming prospects for conservation of marine turtles. One of these is a sudden increase in the demand for calipee by the soup industry. The other is a wholly unexpected resurgence of the market for tortoise shell, or carey.

Calipee is the essential ingredient of clear turtle soup. It is the cartilage of the lower shell. In the marine turtles the armor is lightened for aquatic life by a suppression of the growth of bones which, during the early development of other species of turtles, fuse together into two solid shields, the carapace and the plastron. Even in the sea turtles the spaces at each side of the upper shell tend to be closed by bone as the animal ages, but the openings among the plastral bones remain, and throughout life are covered only by broad scales over an inner layer of cartilage. This cartilage is the calipee.

It is easy to cut out calipee by slicing with a sharp knife around the edges of the space it fills. The pieces thus taken are scraped, washed and dried in the sun. A 300-pound green turtle yields about six pounds of well-dried calipee, but today this may bring prices several times higher than those paid the turtler for the whole animal a few years ago.

THE danger in this new negotiability of calipee is obvious. In former days the mere bulk of the green turtle and the remoteness of its sources were an important protection. Now, chefs in New York and Europe are making turtle soup of no more of the green turtle than calipee, which is a storable product that a man can pack to market on his back or paddle in by dugout, or can hold for the boats that come in sporadically to buy coconuts. Thus, the temptation to the poor fishermen to poach for calipee is strong. And because turtles are most abundant in thinly settled places in which the local need for the meat is quickly satisfied, they are being killed and left to rot for their yield of calipee alone.

The fundamental trouble is that clear green turtle soup is delectable, and that much of its excellence can be achieved using no more of the turtle than the calipee. On a recent short trip to Germany I found "*echte Schildkrötensuppe*" (genuine turtle soup) in six of the eight restaurants in which I had meals. In all it was good, and in one as good as I ever tasted. In all cases the soup was made with calipee adroitly combined with stock of beef or calves' heads, sherry or madeira wine, and the proper spices.

TERRAPIN STEW

Of all the edible North American turtles, the diamondback terrapin of Chesapeake Bay is supposed to make the most delicious stew. Methods of preparation are as varied as the localities from which they come. The following is based on an old recipe from Chesterfield County, Virginia. One six- to seven-inch terrapin serves two. To kill, plunge into boiling, salted water. Parboil for one and a half hours until feet fall off and shell cracks. Remove the turtle and place on its back until cool enough to handle. Discard the heavy part of the intestines, gall and sand bags. Save the liver, small intestines and eggs along with the meat. Pick to pieces. (It is not necessary to bone terrapin.) Cover with boiling water and season highly with pepper, salt, cayenne pepper, hard-boiled egg and lemon. Stew until well done. Just before serving add at least one glass of champagne or sherry.

This growing market for calipee is insidious. Turtles live mostly in unpoliced regions. It is not possible that the poor people there will voluntarily forbear trafficking in them with the rewards so great, and it is not possible to provide the inspection to ensure that only turtles that can be consumed locally are killed for calipee.

A surprising aspect of the problem is that calipee from all the four shelled sea turtles—green turtle, hawksbill, ridley and loggerhead—is acceptable on the market. A soup chef who would sneer at the thought of making his product of any but the finest green turtle meat will cheerfully make the veal-calipee compromise without even asking what kind of calipee it is. In the case of the loggerhead, the new commercial value is not a serious threat. The loggerhead nests mostly along the inhabited shores of the southern United States where it is given fairly effective protection against overt poaching, and where being killed for calipee is a lesser hazard than the solicitous crowds that gather about each female that comes ashore to lay, or than the lights over coastal roads that draw the hatchlings away from the sea, to be mashed by thousands under the wheels of traffic. As for the Atlantic ridley, its nesting place is so remote and its nesting schedule so erratic that it will no doubt remain immune to the new exploitation for a time—although if commercial interests ever do make connection with the ridley *arribadas* on the Mexican coast the slaughter will be unprecedented. In fact, if it should be done with determination an entire species could be wiped out there in two or three seasons. But of all the sea turtles it is the hawksbill that suddenly stands out as a species in critical need of protective attention. The hawksbill nests singly and in scattered small groups in wild places all through the Caribbean and southern Gulf of Mexico. There is therefore no way to concentrate protective surveillance of breeding grounds, as can be done at the green-turtle rookeries. The Caribbean hawksbill is thus hunted both ashore on its widespread nesting beaches and at sea on the reefs and banks where it forages throughout most of the year. During the decades when human populations were spreading so rapidly around the Caribbean, the price of tortoise shell was declining, and the hawksbill has not noticeably diminished in numbers. Now, however, with the market for both carey and calipee expanding, the hawksbill has a double price on its head.

I DO not know what is behind the new demand for carey. There are rumors that it is the Japanese who boosted the price, as their leather industry has raised the pressure on the world's crocodilians as a source of hides. For centuries the Japanese have been the best of all tortoise-shell craftsmen. They are the only ones, I believe, who successfully weld it into blocks of any thickness with no sign of joint planes, even in the honey-clear carey that they esteem so highly. During the 1940s, with the growth of the plastics industry, tortoise shell seemed sure to be superseded. The price of carey fell to almost nothing, and all over the Caribbean *careyeros* turned to other work. When I went to Costa Rica in the summer of 1962, a neighbor at our green-turtle camp who for 20 years had given up his old calling of hawksbill-hunting was back at it again, and his little house had become headquarters for eight other *careyeros* who on every calm day were harpooning hawksbills on a rock bank out in front of the camp. The same thing is happening all through the Caribbean; and in the port towns there are new signs in the windows of export houses, offering to buy calipee and tortoise shell. I seriously doubt that the small world populations of *Eretmochelys* will long survive the unchecked spread of this new commerce.

YOUNG CAIMANS SHOW ONE OF THE DEFENSIVE MEASURES OF THE CROCODILIANS—HIDING AS MUCH OF THEMSELVES IN WATER AS POSSIBLE

Techniques for Survival

Not all of the reptiles are so formidably armored as the turtles, nor so fearsomely toothed as the crocodilians, nor so venomously fanged as many snakes. How, then, do the others take care of themselves? Their methods range from nimble retreats to Houdini escape acts and such ruses as pretending to be big or dead, the last so convincingly played by one snake that it goes through convulsions.

AN ANGRY TOAD-HEADED AGAMID LIZARD FROM ARABIA REARS UP ON ITS HAUNCHES, ITS MOUTH OPEN MENACINGLY AND ITS TAIL CURLED STIFFLY.

Here One Moment, Gone the Next

To escape danger, many reptiles simply run away. Others hide in holes, under rocks and in similar inaccessible spots. A few, however, do not have retreats regularly available to them and must rely on such protective measures as threats and burrowing. The Arabian toad-headed lizard and the South African puff adder, both desert dwellers, bury themselves in sand to elude their enemies. But before wriggling underground, the spunky little lizard assumes a defensive stance and tries to bluff its attacker. If hard put, it will even bite, usually holding on so tightly that its jaws must be pried loose. Another desert lizard of the same family grimaces ferociously, expanding and reddening large folds of skin at the corners of its mouth.

Should the bluff fail, the lizard quickly buries itself by tilting its body from side to side and edging into the sand. At first it plows in with its sloping head, but once under the surface, it arches the neck upward and is in a position to crawl out again after

A SOUTH AFRICAN DWARF PUFF ADDER, RETREATING INTO THE SAND TAILFIRST, SHIMMYS ITS BODY TO SINK BELOW THE SURFACE. AS IT DESCENDS

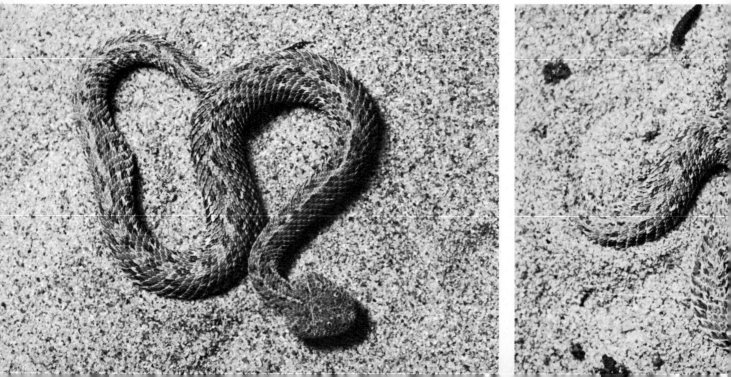

BUT WHEN ITS BLUFF FAILS, IT ROCKS ITS BODY FROM SIDE TO SIDE AND DISAPPEARS HEADFIRST INTO THE SAND, WHISKING ITS TAIL UNDER LAST

the enemy leaves. The horned lizard of the American Southwest buries itself in a similar manner, but often does so to get away from another enemy—the desert sun.

The dwarf puff adder, although equipped with fangs and venom glands that give the back of the head a swollen look, does not stand up to an enemy as the toad-headed lizard does, but wriggles into the sand immediately, leaving a ghost impression behind in the surface. It is aided in its downward retreat by scales which work the grains away from the bottom and sides of its thick body.

The dwarf puff adder's eyes are well protected from irritating grains of sand by the clear shields, or spectacles, covering them, found in all snakes. The toad-headed lizard does not have these shields, but does have scaly "eyebrows" which project out over its eyes, and long scales that fringe the eyelids and serve as lashes. Above ground, these "lashes" help keep wind-blown particles and dust out of the eyes.

VERTICALLY, ITS RASPLIKE SCALES PUSH THE GRAINS OVER ITS BACK. IN THE LAST PHOTOGRAPH, ONLY ITS HEAD AND THE TIP OF ITS TAIL SHOW

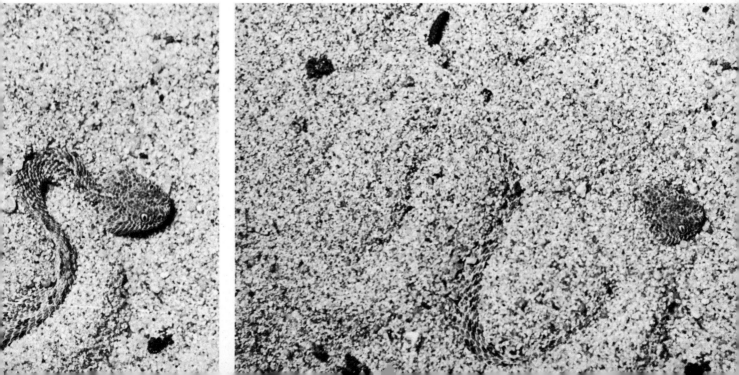

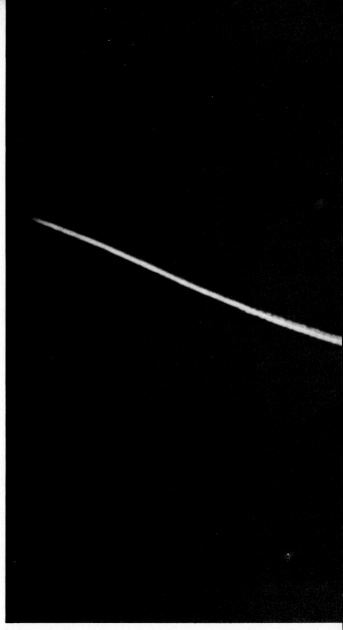

DRACO VOLANS, A FLYING LIZARD OF SOUTHEAST ASIA, EXECUTES A

Fast Runners and Artful Gliders

Survival for many reptiles depends upon the speed of their getaway. The American zebra-tailed and collared lizards, clocked at 16 to 17 miles an hour, are the fastest runners of their group. Along with the crested dragon shown in the motion sequence at left, they are among the few lizards to start off in an upright position. Many other bipedal lizards begin at a trot and as they gain speed rise on their long hind legs and bound off. Some bipedal lizards, such as the Central American basilisk, can even take

THE CRESTED DRAGON, Australia's "bicycle lizard," resorts to a bipedal gait when in a hurry; each stride is two-and-a-half times the body length. The long tail acts as a counterbalance.

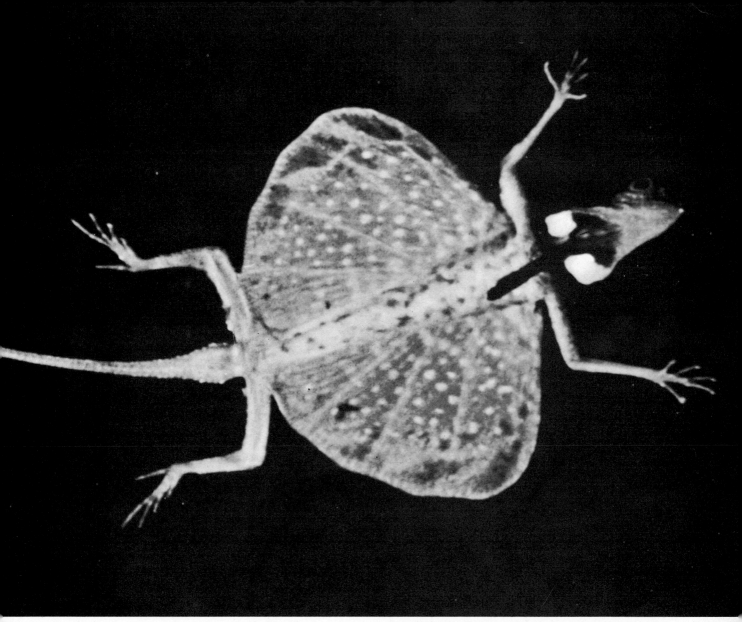

GLIDE. THE "WINGS" MAY BE YELLOW BELOW AND ORANGE AND BLACK ON TOP, OR BURNT UMBER WITH BLACK STRIPES AND MAROON EDGES

several steps on the surface of water before they fall in and swim. No modern reptiles can fly as could the extinct pterosaurs. The nearest they come to true flight is gliding, an art which one lizard genus, *Draco*, the flying dragons, has developed to a considerable state of refinement. Their "wings" are actually folds of scaly membrane supported by five or six pairs of ribs growing from their stick-thin bodies. With these skin flaps outspread, a *Draco* can glide more than 50 feet between tree trunks.

DANGLING from a human hand, a *Draco* reveals its small size. When crawling on a tree, it folds its colorful "wings"—and thus the narrow body looks green all over and blends with the bark.

THE FRILLED LIZARD of Australia is shown in the photograph at upper left resting on a log as a tree snake glides up. In the next photograph, the lizard bobs up hissing and begins to unfurl its umbrellalike frill in an attempt to frighten the intruder. Fully extended (*below*), the frill is yellow, scarlet and steel blue, and in an eight-inch-long specimen may be seven inches wide.

The Intimidators

Several small, inadequately armed reptiles resort to bluffing as a defense. Horned lizards squirt blood, swell up and sometimes bite feebly or inflict wounds with their horns. The lizard opposite meets danger head on, erecting its frill, showing its teeth and occasionally even rearing on its hind legs in an attempt to bite. Other lizards swell brightly colored throat fans. Some bob up and down or rock back and forth.

SPATTERED WITH BLOOD, which it has just squirted from its own eye, a California horned lizard waits for the cornea to clear up. The blood may possibly irritate other animals' eyes.

WAVING A FALSE HEAD, the rubber boa hides its real head among coils of its body. The decoy is actually the blunt tail. When threatened, this small, gentle snake, northernmost rela- tive of the giant boas, rolls up into a protective ball with only the tail sticking out. An enemy will almost invariably bite the wrong end, as evidenced by the scars on this specimen's tail.

FULL OF BRAVADO when first confronted by an aggressor, the harmless eastern hog-nosed snake flattens its neck like a cobra, swells up, waves its tail and hisses loudly.

WHEN ITS BLUFF FAILS, a hog-nose plays dead. It turns on its back, its mouth wide open. To give such "deaths" a realistic touch, hog-noses will often fake convulsions.

RAISING ITS HEAD, a hog-nose peeks to see whether the enemy has left. If righted, it will promptly flop on its back in a limp pose, as though to prove it is still dead.

AT EASE on a leaf, the South African armadillo lizard bears some resemblance to a crocodile. But whereas the crocodile's scales are flat, the lizard's are spiked, especially along the tail.

A Wound-Up Lizard

There is a mythical snake that can put its tail in its mouth and roll along like a hoop. But few people know that there is a real reptile—the armadillo lizard of South Africa—that has perfected such a position as a means of self-defense. And though this lizard cannot roll away over the veld, its projecting spiny scales form an effective stockade around its most vulnerable part—its soft-skinned belly.

When pursued, this slow-moving little lizard, often colored to blend with the sand, heads for a crevice in a rock. Once hidden, it sweeps its tail, which accounts for more than half its length, like a shield around the belly, usually stuffing the tip into its mouth, and lies there. Even a fairly strong pull is not likely to dislodge it. Unlike most lizards, it does not have the "breakaway" tail that they depend on for escape in emergencies. Its tail is firmly attached and will withstand a stiff yank before coming off.

ON THE DEFENSE, the armadillo lizard looks like a wreath. It holds its tail in its mouth with its forefeet, thus protecting the belly from any animals foolish enough to disregard the spines.

A GREEN TURTLE, leaving a trac-
torlike trail in the sand, lumbers
toward the sea after laying her eggs
upbeach. Because of the effort needed to move her great weight, she
often stops and emits a great sigh.

8

A Dubious
Future

IF the world goes on the way it is going it will one day be a world without
reptiles. Some people will accept this calmly, but I mistrust the prospect.
Reptiles are a part of the old wilderness of earth, the environment in which man
got the nerves and hormones that make him human. If we let the reptile go it
is a sign we are ready to let all wilderness go. When that happens we shall no
longer be exactly human.

One of the awesome enigmas of today is how to slow the ruin of the natural
earth while our mindless breeding continues. The ironic fact is that population
control is probably not far off. There is no more need to multiply with the old
fever. There is no more need for barn-raisings and massed infantry. Breeding
is good business, but it is herding our race toward a tragic impasse. When this
is clearly seen and the reproduction is slowed down it will be because thought-
ful people have taken charge; and these people will look about for what has
been left of old values. One of the values is what the human spirit gets from
wilderness, from all kinds of wild original landscapes and beings. The way we
are going, what we keep of the old earth will not be enough to save our honor
with our descendants.

Writing this, I felt one of the qualms you cannot keep down when in your mind you weigh new industries against rough country empty of all but unused beasts and vegetables. I have no real doubts myself, mind you, but to many others in the world, especially the Florida world, to question the complete goodness of population growth is a perverse and sinister sort of iconoclasm that probably should be investigated by a committee. Thinking that way, I scared myself a little, and to get over it I called off the writing for a spell and went over to Jonah's Pond. Jonah's Pond is one of the solid assets of the University of Florida. It is a sinkhole lake with tree-swamp at one end and open water at the other, and all through it a grand confusion of marsh creatures and of floating and emergent plants. The place is a little relic of a vanishing past, and incredibly, it lies on the campus of a university with 13,000 students, less than half a mile from where I am writing now. It is there to go to when euphoria spreads through the press over some new gain the state has made in people.

I went this time to where an alligator called Crooked-jaw has her nest beside a wire fence, at one edge of the swampy end of the lake. I stopped the car and walked over to the nest and looked at it closely. I had taken a picture of it the day before, and I could see that Crooked-jaw had made some changes during the night. They were not drastic—only small, fastidious adjustments to show she knew the heap was warming a new generation of her kind. A root-mass of buttonbush had been added, and a few live switches of *Decodon*, and some scooped-up slush of coontail from the bottom. On the top of the pile was a single balled-up pink paper towel; and though it seems unlikely, I am sure I had seen this lying six feet to one side of the nest the day before. I can say that because I was aroused at the sight of it, at the idea of anybody defiling with pink the premises of an alligator nest. Crooked-jaw clearly failed to share my resentment. There is no accounting for tastes. The nest did not look as good to me with the paper towel on it, but the matter was not in my hands.

The alligator was not in her usual station, her lying-in pool, as it were—the little dredged-out hole of water a mother gator waits in for eggs to hatch. She was off somewhere among the floating islands, and I started croaking, *eer-rump*, *eer-rump*, like a little gator croaking. A long way out through the flooded willows a floating island began to quake; and then all at once water surged out from the frogbit raft beside the waiting pool, and Crooked-jaw came up looking at me. A gallinule whined from a bonnet patch, and in the high haze to the west the sand-hill cranes were bugling. I croaked some more, but the alligator had lost interest. She sank into the water till her chin rested on the mud, and only the bumps of her eyes and nose and the big scales of her back stuck out.

LOOKING at her there in her fragment of a doomed landscape, I was sure again that the saving of parts of the primitive earth has got to be done, and that it has got to be done without trying to justify it on practical grounds. Species and landscapes must be kept because it pleases people to contemplate them, and because freer men of future times will be appalled if we irresponsibly let them go. Not facing that fact seems to me the great weakness in the outlook for wilderness preservation today.

It will take resolute people to put abstract values in place of material progress. In testing the mettle and conscience of recruits for the work, the reptile—particularly the unloved, legless snake—may serve as a sort of shibboleth. A man who feels in his bones that snakes must be kept in the woods will be proper stuff for the struggle coming.

TWO IN A BURROW

A sooty shearwater and a tuatara peer from a nesting burrow dug by the bird. These two animals often live together in harmony. Their cohabitation is made easy through much of the year by their routines: usually the bird is off fishing during the day and the tuatara out foraging at night. When the bird migrates, the tuatara hibernates in the burrow.

Snakes are probably disappearing at a more rapidly rising rate than any other group of vertebrates. Besides the widespread antipathy they get from man, marshes are drained, country is reforested in pure stands of unsuitable cover, poisons spread abroad kill off the food supplies of the creatures snakes eat, and even kill the snakes themselves. But the most spectacular thing happening to snakes is the onslaught of cars on the roads. Twenty years ago, in his book *That Vanishing Eden*, Thomas Barbour spoke of the passing of snakes before cars on the roads of Florida, but he never saw the big change. It came with the many-laned highways of the '50s and '60s.

THE worst snake traps are the causeways across marshes and the streams of cars that cross them. Snakes are lured to them to enjoy the warm paving, or to escape flooded habitat, or merely in the course of their foraging. I remember a vast dying of snakes on the road across Paynes Prairie two decades ago, when man and weather chanced to move together against the creatures of the marsh. On October 18, 1941, a hurricane moved in from the gulf and spun in the vicinity for 36 hours, bringing 14 inches of rain during five days. The prairie changed from a marsh to a lake and the water rose so high that only the tips of the tallest grasses showed. On the 25th some students brought in 200 snakes they had caught along the road-fill and told of a great hegira of snakes, and of congregations of buzzards squabbling over the dead ones mashed by passing cars. There was clearly something extraordinary going on, and four of us from the biology department went out to investigate. We started at the northern edge of the prairie and walked abreast down the road with flashlights, one of us at each guardrail and two along the middle of the pavement. The road over the marsh was two miles long. We counted every snake dead or alive between the guardrails, which in those single-lane days were 20 feet apart. We picked up 723 snakes in the two miles, about two thirds of them dead or injured.

As an accumulation of several days, this number of casualties would not have been unprecedented. But these were the accumulation of no more than the four hours or so since sundown. During the daylight hours buzzards—black vultures and turkey vultures—had been attracted to the killing by the hundreds and had carried the dead snakes away almost as fast as they were run over. So the snakes we counted had been killed after dark. The tally was: 64 banded water snakes; 85 green water snakes; 55 garter snakes; 200 ribbon snakes; six brown snakes; three king snakes; 284 red-bellied snakes; 19 Allen's mud snakes; three horn snakes; four cottonmouth moccasins.

The slaughter had no noticeable effect on the levels of snake populations in the prairie. For a decade afterward the road remained a mecca for snake collectors, and they kept coming from distant places to walk along it with bag and stick. But in recent years the prairie snakes have declined. Although the roadside was made a wildlife sanctuary not long ago, and the snakes in it are now immune to people who used to take them away in sacks, the cars keep going by, and snakes have no immunity to them.

At the end of Chapter 2, I held up the New Zealand tuatara as a sort of sign of the paleontologic waning of reptiles—a symbol of their decline since the roaring Mesozoic when their forefathers browbeat a cowering world. This same lonesome wisp of a reptilian remnant also tells a story of reptiles against men. The tuatara, even more than snakes, gives the precarious feel of the hold that useless wild things have on the world. I want to dwell a little upon what is known about a creature that is unique and one so wholly at the mercy of a few people of good will, the New Zealanders who have made a preserve of the tuatara islands.

This loneliest reptile in the world, known technically as *Sphenodon puncta-tus*, looks like a stocky, big-headed lizard. The males average about two feet long and weigh about two pounds. Females are a good deal shorter and only half as heavy. The common name, tuatara, is a Maori word that means spiny, and refers to a low, toothed crest down the neck and back. A few hundred years ago there were tuataras on mainland New Zealand, and the Maoris ate them. Today they live only on 20 cliff-bound islets off the New Zealand coast—the only representative of an order with one of the smallest geographic ranges of any vertebrate animal.

ALTHOUGH *Sphenodon* looks like a lizard, it clearly is not. It differs from lizards in many ways. One of the most arresting is in the lack of any copulatory organ. Even more engrossing, to the paleontologist at least, is the presence of two complete bony arcades in the temporal region of the skull, as in the ancient diapsid reptiles. Recent evidence suggests that the open-sided skull of lizards probably is a modification of this old two-arcade style. So the tuatara appears to fade back into the ancestral line of the lizards and snakes. The wonder is how little it has changed in the millions of years that lizards and snakes were evolving so variously.

One of the features of *Sphenodon* that used to be considered distinctive is a third, or median, eye, located on top of the head but roofed over by the skin. Although this organ has the lens, retina and nerve connections that go with light-reception, there are no eye muscles or other apparatus for accommodation or focusing, and experiments indicate that no seeing is done with the eye. Its function, if it still has any, is thus unknown. In any case, the median eye is not peculiar to *Sphenodon*. It occurs in various modern lizards too, and may be used by them in their behavioral temperature control. In some fossil reptiles it was much more strongly developed and perhaps used for vision.

The female tuatara lays from eight to 15 soft-shelled eggs, each a little over an inch long. The nest is a pit in well-drained soil, dug and covered by the female. The period of incubation is 15 months, which is far longer than that of most other reptiles. The tuatara is one of the rare reptiles with a true voice, and has been heard to croak dolefully on misty nights or on becoming annoyed with a captor. It seems to take 20 years to reach sexual maturity. This, and the slow growth rates that have been recorded, lead to the belief that it may attain ages of a century or more.

The tuatara today is mainly insectivorous and nocturnal. It has been observed foraging in temperatures as low as 45° Fahrenheit. It lives in intimate association with the sea birds that swarm on the islands. The birds keep the underbrush broken down and manure the soil heavily, and an abundant insect fauna lives in it. One of the bird associates, a petrel, digs burrows. The tuatara regularly occupies these, sometimes moving in before the petrel is through incubating eggs or raising chicks. The association is not obligatory, however, and some tuataras dig their own burrows.

The sparse tuatara community reveals ecologic relationships with singular clarity. Although the long-term survival of the tuatara may never be explained, it is easy to see why the creature is able to hold on now. Its inaccessible islands, with their bird colony and salt-forest habitat, are a remote asylum where an ancient type, elsewhere replaced by more nimble lizards and mammals, can live on in ancestral ways. The sun goes on spilling into the cold sea. The plankton catch up the energy of sunshine and multiply, and feed the teeming fishes. The petrels, terns, cormorants and penguins swarm out from the islets and harvest the fields of fish, and then go back and leave their droppings on the ground under the scrub where they roost and nest and where the tuatara lives. The guano grows thick and odorous and the insects thrive. There is food and peace on the islets, and *Sphenodon* lives on, anachronistic but safe for a while.

In some ways the tuatara is an ideal model for preservation practice. Like any animal, it is part of a community. Unlike most animals, however, its community is a simple one that can easily be understood and kept free of disorganizing influences. The economic value of both the animal and its environment is quite small, and above all, the tuatara is a fantastically appropriate example of the last of a kind—the very last of an order older than the dinosaurs that vanished an eon ago. The one grave defect in its case as a triumph of wilderness preservation is that the effort involved in saving it should have been so slight. Saving the tuatara required only laws protecting the animal itself, and the removal of a few sheep that hurt the habitat. That way, it is a bad lesson. No significant preserving of nature can be done with slight sacrifice. The true test will come when great sacrifices are needed, when it becomes necessary to fight the indifference of most of the world and the active opposition of much of it, to surmount man's ingrained determination to put the far future out of his mind in matters of current profit.

BESIDES the inherent technical difficulties of wilderness conservation, the effort to save original nature faces a whole constellation of other kinds of problems. The easiest obstacle to recognize is the opposition by people who oppose the keeping of wilderness for material reasons. These people would shape the world into an ant hill; they are clearly mad. It is unthinkable that they will much longer control the destiny of the race. There is another block of humanity that simply does not care; and an unsorted lot who think of themselves as conservationists, and who in one way or another are, but who are not facing the really tough obligation at all. I refer to all people who think of saving nature for meat, water, timber or picnic grounds for the future; and to the hunters who hope their grandsons will get red blood by shooting things, and to the reverence-for-life cultists who are foredoomed to inconsistency, and to the biologists who resist the loss of material for study, and to keepers of zoological gardens who preserve nature in cages. Putting this mixture of motives and aspirations together under the label conservation has made, in some cases, a temporarily stronger front. But it has muddied the real issue, hidden the dimensions of the long job and kept everybody from articulating the awful certainty that the hard saving has got to be done for the sake of abstract values.

For several years I have been involved in a preservation program which, like the tuatara project, has been atypically feasible—although for different reasons. This is a campaign to rehabilitate the green turtle in the Caribbean Sea, where its once extensive nesting range has been reduced to only two rookery beaches.

The green sea turtle, *Chelonia mydas*, is the most important source of human food among the reptiles and the most valuable reptile in the world. Historically, its economic role is conspicuous, and in the planning to raise the food production of the oceans it offers strong promise. Its potential is based on the fact that it eats plants, and tends to aggregate wherever submerged marine vegetation —several spermatophytes and a few kinds of algae—grow in more or less continuous stands. Today most such underwater pastures are unused by any but

THE HELPFUL BIRDS

The tuatara's existence on its remote islands is made possible by sea birds like the cormorants shown above. They cover the ground and rocks with their droppings, creating an ideal environment for the development of a large population of ground insects such as beetles and crickets. These are the tuatara's main source of food, and it forages for them at night (below).

the tiniest of marine animals, but there is evidence that they were once extensively grazed by green turtles. The decline was evidently due mainly to human depredations on the nesting grounds.

Probably the greatest concentration of nesting green turtles in the world, and certainly the most intensively exploited and soundly regulated nesting colony, is in the Sarawak Islands of Borneo. Here Tom Harrisson, curator of the Sarawak Museum, has studied the colony for years, and his researches and the recent intensive investigations of John R. Hendrickson of the University of Malaya have laid the groundwork for a sound program of management of the rookery. The Sarawak turtles are not killed; only a carefully set proportion of the eggs is taken. The yield of the rookery has generally been between one and two million eggs for the dozen years or so that good records have been kept.

In the Caribbean, the way things were going a short while ago, the green turtle was facing complete extirpation. Now I believe there is no such danger. Instead there is even the prospect that this once threatened species will become a resource of major importance. The change in outlook was made possible by a combination of circumstances such as cannot be counted on in most preservation projects. In the first place, the suspected migratory feats of green turtles focused scientific interest on them and brought support from research foundations—the National Science Foundation and the Office of Naval Research—for studies of their basic natural history. Another factor favoring the intervention was the historic and potential importance of the animal as human food. Still another was its evident amenability to management as a harvester of great areas of marine vegetation that otherwise would go to waste. A final factor that has greatly eased the way is the lucky circumstance that the single nesting beach remaining in the western Caribbean is located at Tortuguero, on the coast of that gem of a small nation, the Republic of Costa Rica. In former times exploitation of the Tortuguero colony brought Costa Rica a steady small revenue in the form of a fee paid by the concessionaire, who parceled out the beach to the turtlers and sold their catch to the caiman schooners or sent it away as deckloads on freight boats going back to Florida. But in 1957 the government closed the beach to exploitation. The move saved the green turtle for the western Caribbean, but at the same time it deprived Costa Rica of all profit from its green turtles, because there is no good turtle pasture along the Costa Rican shore and no turtles go there except during the breeding season. The refuge will repopulate the pastures from Colombia to Mexico, and will increase the yield of the turtle grounds of the Nicaraguan Miskitia to schooners turtling for the markets of New York and Europe. For Costa Rica itself there is only the satisfaction of having faced the choice between quick gain and a better future—and having chosen with characteristic wisdom.

In 1955, when the first of a series of grants from the National Science Foundation was made, a tagging camp was established at Tortuguero. The information accumulated helped stimulate the founding of the Caribbean Conservation Corporation, a nonprofit undertaking dedicated to restoring the Atlantic green turtle in American waters. This is the strongest effort, I suppose, ever made in behalf of any reptile. The effort began to grow when Joshua B. Powers, an international publishers' representative with a long-time interest in Latin America and its people, read my book, *The Windward Road*, in which I told of the history and plight of the Caribbean green turtle and of its potential as a renewed source of food. As a result, Josh Powers founded The Brotherhood of the Green

Turtle, a fraternity of influential people who gathered about the idea of finding a way to save the Caribbean green turtle. The movement attracted the attention of John H. Phipps, a Florida philanthropist and conservationist, and with his support the Caribbean Conservation Corporation took shape and went to work. It is now in its third year of operation.

The current aim of the organization is to re-establish breeding colonies of *Chelonia* in the places where they once were. To this end, eggs from a two-mile section of the Tortuguero beach are placed in artificial nests in a wire enclosure where they are free of the usual hazards that attend incubation and hatching. After about two months the young turtles begin erupting from the sand and are placed in tanks of sea water and fed on chopped fish until distribution time. The United States Navy has assisted in the distribution. The Caribbean Sea Frontier sent down an amphibian airplane from Roosevelt Roads, Puerto Rico, to carry batches of hatchlings—45,000 so far—to introduction sites all around the Caribbean and in Florida and the Bahamas.

The restoration project is a gamble. There is no way to be sure the planted hatchlings will go back to the introduction site when they reach maturity. They may fall back into the ancestral cycle of reproductive travel, and return to Tortuguero instead. This chance must be taken. Results with salmon suggest that young fish are imprinted by some sensory experience at the site of introduction, and that this impression overrides any tendency to return to the ancestral spawning ground, but instead draws them to the new locality to nest. It is the hope that young green turtles will do the same. Meanwhile, the protection being given the Costa Rican nesting ground is the one factor preventing the loss of the green turtle from the western Caribbean.

Another field in which the information provided by the green turtle investigations will be useful is turtle farming. The submarine plants the green turtle feeds on grow in pure stands in shallow water behind reefs, or on shelves among islands. Some of these places lend themselves to being easily fenced. In such enclosed natural pastures, green turtles could be kept like aquatic cattle. The Caribbean Conservation Corporation is planning pilot projects of this kind. If they are successful, the green turtle may become one of the first marine vertebrates to be successfully cultured for food.

WHEN I hear of a new idea for raising the food yield of the sea—or of the land for that matter—I have mixed feelings. I hate to see any comfort come to those who encourage the useless multiplication of man. But there are very hungry people in places where green turtles once were abundant and are now unknown. It is the sea that will be called on to feed these people, as well as the hordes of our descendants. And anyway, when you save a species for meat you are bound to save useless bits of wilderness to go along with it. So whenever a bit of the waning world can be saved for meat, then go ahead and do it that way. But inadvertent saving of scraps will never keep off the ruin of the earth. The only way is to name the real obligation clearly, to say without hedging that no price can be set for the things that have to be preserved.

When New Zealand set up the *Sphenodon* preserve I wish they had said it was not to placate zoologists, but so that plain men could go on singing the tuatara out of its hole. Casting about for old accounts of the tuatara in New Zealand, I found these five sentences from a 1903 issue of the *Lyttelton Times*, quoted by James Hutton and Frederick Wollaston Drummond in their book, *The Animals of New Zealand:*

"The tuatara lizards at the Opaiva fisheries seem to be susceptible to music. They will come out of their holes to hear a song, when nothing else will induce them to appear. They prefer a good rousing chorus rather than a solo. Some time ago a number of visitors to the hatcheries wanted to see the tuataras, which, however, refused to come forth until a little girl sang 'Soldiers of the Queen,' and others joined in the chorus. The sound seemed to have appealed to the reptiles, and they responded by showing themselves to the singers."

Ask a New Zealander why he saved the tuatara and he no doubt will think the question silly, and say because it's one of a kind, and because zoologists are partial to the beast and because once gone it would be lost forever. And all that is so. But the same can be said of all reptiles, with only the time shifted about a bit. The New Zealanders are responsible for the tuatara, and the world is responsible for reptiles. The only difference is the New Zealanders came to grips with their problem sooner. The problem itself was far, far simpler. It was so simple and clear-cut, and the material sacrifice so negligible that no really searching appraisal of values had to be made.

Basically, what you have to do is go ahead and admit that tuataras must be saved so that people can sing them out of holes. Only then are you ready for the harder jobs, like justifying a future for snakes, which have no legs, hear no music and badly clutter subdivisions. Bore through to the core of what is required and you see that it is an aggressive stewardship of relics, of samples of original order, of objects and organizations of cosmic craft. This work will take stanch people, and the reptile can be the shibboleth by which they pass.

To get the real feel of the problem, I conjure up a man of some far future time, walking in a last woods lying unruined among launching pads of a planetary missile terminal, and coming astounded upon the last of all living individuals of *Crotalus adamanteus*, the great unruly diamondback rattlesnake. It is a full-grown female snake that I see, two yards long, stern of face, and all marked off in geometric velvet. It is the sort of being that always, inadvertently and without malice, has been a thorn in the flesh of Americans, one of the novel terrors the land held for men whether they came in caravels or wandered down into the New World out of the snake-free Siberian cold. Seeing the man, this last diamondback begins readying the steel of its coils, and they ebb and flow behind the thin neck holding the broad head steady and still, except for the long tongue waving. By the girth of her I judge that this is a pregnant snake, heavy with some dozens of prehatched perfect little snakes the same as herself, all venomous and indignant from the start, all intractable and, like their mother, unable to live except as free snakes.

The snake that confronts the imagined man is a moving thing to see. It is not easy to understand all the feelings aroused by such a sight, and the snake I think forward to is the last in all the pablum agar culture of the purified world. The coils of her body rise and fall in slow spirals, the keen singing of her rattle sounds, and she waits there, testing with the forks of her tongue the whole future of her kind. In my thought the man then stoops with an old urge and picks up a stick. It is almost the only stick left lying in the eastern half of North America, and the man takes it up and moves in closer to the wondering snake. He raises the stick, then somehow lowers it as if in thought, then halfway brings it up again. And then the conjuring fails for me, and the snake song falls away, like the song of cicadas losing heart, one by one. The woods grow dark and fade off into distant times.

A LONE, FULLY GROWN TUATARA, PERHAPS A CENTURY OLD, CROAKS ITS PLAINTIVE SONG FROM THE SAFETY OF ITS BLEAK ISLAND REFUGE

Twilight of the Reptiles

It has taken some 150 million years of paleontological disasters to reduce the immense diversity of reptilian life to a meager four orders. But it has taken man only a few hundred years of indiscriminate slaughtering to bring many survivors to the brink of complete extinction. Belatedly, in some areas of the world, conservationists are now studying ways to save these relics of the distant past.

Chosen for Survival

Because they are no longer eaten and their hides have no commercial value, and because they inhabit clusters of remote islands which neither men nor other large predators want, the less than 10,000 remaining tuataras enjoy the protection of conservationists. But the species also has its own formidable survival equipment. This includes the ability to keep active at extremely low body temperatures, an adaptation well suited to its cool climate, and a relatively low metabolism, which means it can get along on a reduced diet—usually insects, worms and snails.

A MATURE MALE weighs about two pounds and reaches a length of two feet; adult females are shorter and weigh only half as much. Handlers need not fear; tuataras are harmless to man.

CLOAKED IN GLOOM, Stephens Island is the most thoroughly studied habitat of tuataras. A square mile of cloud-capped land, it rises in sheer cliffs 1,000 feet above the waters of Cook Strait, New Zealand.

TAIL REGENERATION, which tuataras share with many lizards, takes several years. A broken tail *(top)* will replace itself with a tail of a different texture *(center)* or, occasionally, with a forked tail *(bottom)*.

A CLOUD OF SAND rises behind a female green turtle excavating her nest on an Australian Great Barrier Reef beach. She excavates with all four flippers until her shell is level with the surface of the beach. She then uses her rear flippers to dig a deeper hole for her eggs. Since her eggs are prized by the local population, many will not be incubated long enough to hatch.

A COUPLE OF HATCHLINGS scramble out of the nest. They must now run a perilous gantlet to the sea while hungry birds swoop down upon them and predaceous fishes wait below.

Candidates for Extinction

Unlike the tuatara, some of the more common aquatic turtles have been fair game for primitive hunters and patrician gourmets alike for centuries. From the Great Barrier Reef islands of Australia to Venezuela's Orinoco River, turtle eggs are harvested in the tens of millions. In the Caribbean thousands of turtles are killed for their flesh, while others are shipped abroad for processing. Just a few years ago, 5,000 Caribbean marine turtles were transformed into 600,000 quarts of soup annually by one New York City firm. And there is still a market for "tortoise-shell" (actually turtle-shell) ornaments. With so much slaughter and so little conservation, the sea turtles' long history may soon be concluded.

A BUTCHERED FEMALE has her egg clusters removed and placed inside a tin can by a native of the island of Mer, near New Guinea. Both the meat and eggs are highly prized by the people of the southwest Pacific. On the little island of Talang Talang off Borneo, for example, it has been estimated that close to two million turtle eggs have been collected in a single year.

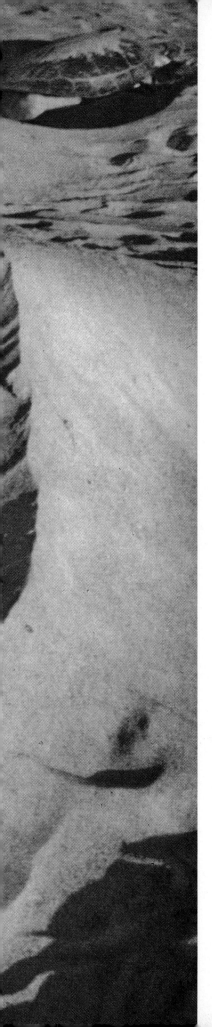

A SWARM OF FEMALE RIVER TURTLES AWAITS A COVER OF DARKNESS BEFORE BEACHING

Hope for the River Turtles

The South American river turtles may yet escape the fate of total annihilation, despite the 48 million eggs and countless adults and hatchlings pillaged each year by local Indian raids on their island nesting places. A long-range study program is now under way in which eggs and hatchlings are counted, young turtles are branded and breeding schedules recorded. Conservationists hope to discover the most beneficial population level for the turtles and to control the take at a level below the minimum number necessary to the species' survival.

DEEP IN THEIR CATCH, Venezuelan natives load their small boats with live turtles. Those not eaten will be sold. The high toll taken of river turtles is made possible because they congregate at the same places year after year for breeding and nesting.

DEEP IN HER NEST, a tardy female hurries to complete her excavation as the sun rises over a beach on the Orinoco River. Digging the nest, laying and covering the eggs and returning to the river are usually completed between sunset and dawn.

CONSERVATIONISTS MARK AN ORINOCO RIVER NESTING SITE WITH STAKES. THE EGGS WILL BE REMOVED TO A SAFE PLACE FOR INCUBATION

HATCHLING TURTLES that have just been branded are released by Dr. Janis Roze, a biologist with the University of Venezuela. Instinctively, these creatures scramble toward the Orinoco.

BRANDING THE YOUNG provides a record of growth for turtles captured later on. Branding also reveals distribution patterns and the frequency of visits to nesting places.

VISUAL TRACKING experiment, designed to supply information about female sea-turtle navigation during nesting, is attempted with balloons attached to their shells.

Bibliography

General Herpetology

†Bellairs, Angus d'A., *Reptiles: Life History, Evolution and Structure*. Harper Torchbooks, 1960.

Bellairs, A., and R. Carrington, *The World of Reptiles*. American Elsevier, 1966.

Goin, Coleman J., and Olive Goin, *Introduction to Herpetology*. W. H. Freeman, 1962.

Mertens, Robert, *The World of Amphibians and Reptiles*. McGraw-Hill, 1960.

Oliver, James, *The Natural History of North American Amphibians and Reptiles*. Van Nostrand, 1955.

Schmidt, Karl P., *A Check List of North American Amphibians and Reptiles*. American Society of Ichthyologists and Herpetologists, 1953.

Schmidt, Karl P., and Robert F. Inger, *Living Reptiles of the World*. Doubleday, 1957.

*Zim, Herbert S., and Hobart M. Smith, *Reptiles and Amphibians*. Golden Press, 1953.

Anatomy and Physiology

†Ashley, L. M., *Laboratory Anatomy of the Turtle*. William C. Brown, 1955.

Romer, Alfred S., *Osteology of the Reptiles*. University of Chicago Press, 1956.

Young, J. Z., *The Life of Vertebrates*. Oxford University Press, London, 1962.

Evolution and Fossils

Colbert, Edwin H., *Dinosaurs: Their Discovery and Their World*. E. P. Dutton, 1961. *Evolution of the Vertebrates*. John Wiley & Sons, 1955.

Fenton, Carroll L., and Mildred A. Fenton, *Fossil Book*. Doubleday, 1958.

*Goodrich, Edwin S., *Studies on the Structure and Development of Vertebrates* (Vols. I and II). Dover, 1958.

Romer, Alfred S., *Vertebrate Paleontology*. University of Chicago Press, 1945. *The Vertebrate Story*. University of Chicago Press, 1959.

*Simpson, George G., *The Meaning of Evolution*. Yale University Press, 1949.

Turtles and Crocodilians

Carr, Archie, *Handbook of Turtles of the United States, Canada, and Baja California*. Comstock Publishing, 1952.

McIlhenny, E. A., *The Alligator's Life History*. Christopher, 1935.

Parsons, James J., *Green Turtle and Man*. University of Florida Press, 1962.

Pope, Clifford H., *Turtles of the United States and Canada*. Alfred A. Knopf, 1939.

Snakes and Lizards

Klauber, Laurence M., *Rattlesnakes* (Vols. I and II). University of California Press, 1956.

Morris, Ramona and Desmond, *Men and Snakes*. McGraw-Hill, 1965.

Parker, H. W., *Snakes*. Norton, 1963.

Pope, Clifford H., *The Giant Snakes*. Alfred A. Knopf, 1961. *The Poisonous Snakes of the New World*. New York Zoological Society, 1944.

Schmidt, Karl P., and D. Dwight Davis, *Field Book of Snakes of the United States and Canada*. G. P. Putnam's Sons, 1941.

Smith, Hobart M., *Handbook of Lizards of the United States and Canada*. Comstock Publishing, 1946.

Wright, Albert H., and Anna A. Wright, *Handbook of Snakes of the United States and Canada*. Comstock Publishing, 1957.

Regional Guides

Alvarez del Toro, Miguel, *Reptiles de Chiapas*. Instituto Zoologico, Tuxtla Gutiérrez, Mexico, 1960.

Anderson, Paul, *Reptiles of Missouri*. University of Missouri Press, 1965.

Barrett, Charles, *Reptiles of Australia*. Cassell & Co., Ltd., London, 1950.

Breckenridge, W. J., *Reptiles and Amphibians of Minnesota*. University of Minnesota Press, 1949.

Brown, Bryce C., *An Annotated Check List of Reptiles and Amphibians of Texas*. Baylor University Press, 1950.

Cansdale, G. S., *West African Snakes*. Longmans, 1961.

Carr, Archie, and Coleman J. Goin, *Guide to the Reptiles, Amphibians, and Freshwater Fishes of Florida*. University of Florida Press, 1959.

Conant, Roger, *A Field Guide to Reptiles and Amphibians of the United States and Canada East of the 100th Meridian*. Houghton Mifflin, 1958. †*Reptiles and Amphibians of the Northeastern States*. Philadelphia Zoological Society, 1957. *The Reptiles of Ohio*. University of Notre Dame Press, 1951.

Deraniyagala, P.E.P., *A Colored Atlas of Some Vertebrates from Ceylon. Tetrapod Reptilia* (Vol. 2). Ceylon Government Press, 1953. *Serpentoid Reptilia* (Vol. 3). Ceylon Government Press, 1955.

FitzSimons, Vivian F. M., *Snakes of Southern Africa*. Ginn & Co., 1962.

Khalaf, Kamel T., *Reptiles of Iraq with Some Notes on the Amphibians*. Ar-Rabitta Press, Baghdad, 1959.

Kinghorn, J. R., *The Snakes of Australia*. Michigan State University Press, 1956.

Leeson, Frank, *Identification of Snakes of the Gold Coast*. Oliver and Boyd, Ltd., London, 1950.

Logier, E. B. S., *The Snakes of Ontario*. University of Toronto Press, 1958.

Logier, E. B. S., and G. C. Toner, *A Check List of Amphibians and Reptiles of Canada and Alaska*. Royal Ontario Museum, 1961.

Loveridge, Arthur, *Reptiles of the Pacific World*. Macmillan, 1946.

Maki, Moichiro, *Monograph of the Snakes of Japan*. Dai-ichi Shobo, Tokyo, 1931.

McCauley, Robert H., *The Reptiles of Maryland and the District of Columbia*. Published by the author, 1945.

Mertens, Robert, and Heinz Wermuth, *Die Amphibien und Reptilien Europas*. Kramer, Frankfurt, 1960.

Pope, Clifford H., *The Reptiles of China*. American Museum of Natural History, 1935.

Rose, Walter, *Reptiles and Amphibians of Southern Africa*. Bailey Bros. & Swinfen, Ltd., London, 1954.

Smith, Hobart, *Handbook of Amphibians and Reptiles of Kansas*. University of Kansas Museum of Natural History, Miscellaneous Publication, No. 9, 1956.

Smith, Malcom, *The British Amphibians and Reptiles*. Collins, London, 1951.

Smith, Philip W., *The Amphibians and Reptiles of Illinois*. Illinois Natural History Survey Bulletin, 1961.

Stebbins, Robert C., *Field Guide to the Western Reptiles and Amphibians*. Houghton Mifflin, 1966. *Amphibians and Reptiles of Western North America*. McGraw-Hill, 1954.

Tweedie, M. W. F., *The Snakes of Malaya*. Government Printing Office, Singapore, 1957.

Worrell, Eric, *Reptiles of Australia*. Tri-Ocean Books, 1963.

Miscellaneous

Darlington, Philip J. Jr., *Zoogeography*. John Wiley & Sons, 1957.

Hesse, Richard, W. C. Allee, and K. P. Schmidt, eds., *Ecological Animal Geography*. John Wiley & Sons, 1951.

How to Care for Reptiles

†Dowling, Herndon G., and Stephen Spencock, *The Care of Pet Turtles*. New York Zoological Society, 1960.

†Greenberg, Blanche, *Pet Chameleons*. All Pets, 1958.

Roberts, Mervin F., *Alligators and Crocodilians as Pets*. T. F. H. Publications, 1958. *Turtles as Pets*. T. F. H. Publications, 1960.

†Smith, Hobart, *Snakes as Pets*. All Pets, 1958.

*Also available in paperback.
†Only available in paperback.

Credits

The sources for the illustrations in this book are shown below. Credits for pictures from left to right are separated by commas, top to bottom by dashes.

Cover—Nina Leen
8—Allan Grant
10—Lowell Hess
11—Matt Greene
12—Lowell Hess
13—Rene Martin
14,15—Eva Cellini
17—Z.J. Leszczyneki
18,19—Jack J. Kunz
20,21—John Markham, James R. Simon from Photo Researchers, Inc.—John Gerard from National Audubon Society
22, 23—Russ Kinne from Photo Researchers, Inc.—Eliot Elisofon, Dmitri Kessel
24—Richard G. Zweifel
25—John H. Tashjian—N. Cohen
26,27—Lisa Larsen, Harold Pollock from Freelance Photographers Guild—Dr. Robert S. Simmons
28,29,30—N. Cohen
31—R. Van Nostrand for the San Diego Zoo
32,33—Matt Greene, John Markham
34—Herbert Gehr
36,38,39—Stephen Rogers Peck
40,41—Sy Barlow
43—Walter Sanders
44,45—Lowell Hess
46,47—drawings by Mark A. Binn courtesy American Museum of Natural History

48,49—Mark A. Binn courtesy American Museum of Natural History except top Walter Sanders
50,51—Courtesy American Museum of Natural History, courtesy Peabody Museum of Natural History
52—Isabelle Hunt Conant
55—Frances W. Zweifel
56,59—Matt Greene
60—John Norris Wood
63—Loomis Dean
64,65—Carl Gans, Dr. Robert S. Simmons
66,67,68—Nina Leen
69—Nina Leen—Lee Boltin
70,71—Nina Leen
72—Jay Leviton from Black Star
73—Bernard Hoffman—Walker Van Riper
74,75—Rene Martin
76, 77—Paul Popper except right Alan Bruce and Carl Gans
78—Raymond Bridgman Cowles
80—Matt Greene
82—Rene Martin
84,85—Frances W. Zweifel
87—Rene Martin
89—John Mitchell
90,91—painting by Mel Brindle
92—Loomis Dean
93—Lee Boltin
94,95—Loomis Dean—William Vandivert

96, 97—N. Cohen—Bucky Reeves, Loomis Dean
98—Walter Dawn—John Mitchell
99—R. Van Nostrand for the San Diego Zoo
100,101—Isabelle Hunt Conant
102—John Gerard from Monkmeyer Press Photo Service
103—Denis Brihat from Rapho-Guillumette
104—Fred Ward from Black Star
106—Stephen Rogers Peck
108,109—John Norris Wood
110—Rene Martin
115—Russ Kinne from Photo Researchers, Inc.
116—Shelley Grossman—Nina Leen
117—Shelley Grossman—Alfred Eisenstaedt
118—Shelley Grossman
119—H.G. Cogger, Larry Burrows
120—N. Cohen
121—H. Heusser
122—Shelley Grossman except top Francis Miller
123—Francis Miller
124—Fritz Goro
126—Hans Zillessen
131—Eva Cellini
133—Mark A. Binn
135—Combine
136—G.E. Kirkpatrick for the San Diego Zoo

137—Walter Dawn
138,139—Charles H. Hackenbrock, Archie Carr—Dr. Robert S. Simmons
140,141—Mel Hunter
142,143—Dr. Robert S. Simmons—Lynwood Chase from National Audubon Society, Leonard Lee Rue III from Monkmeyer Press Photo Service
144,145—Dr. Robert S. Simmons
146—Pierre Boulat
149—Enid Kotschnig
152,153—Matt Greene
157—Annan Photo Features
158, 159—top Standard Oil Co., New Jersey; bottom Mertens
160,161—Peter Stackpole except left R.C. Snyder
162—Fritz Goro
163—John H. Tashjian—N. Cohen
164,165—Richard G. Zweifel except right Nina Leen
166—Cy La Tour, N. Cohen
168—Fritz Goro
170, 173—Hans Zillessen
177, 178, 179—W.H. Dawbin and M.D. King
180—Fritz Goro—Photo Mahuzier
181—Fritz Goro
182, 183, 184—Dr. Janis Roze
185—Ralph J. Sneeringer
Back Cover—Matt Greene

Acknowledgments

The editors of this book are particularly indebted to Richard G. Zweifel, Curator, Department of Herpetology, The American Museum of Natural History, who read the book in its entirety. They are also indebted to Charles M. Bogert, Chairman and Curator, Department of Herpetology, The American Museum of Natural History; Nathan W. Cohen, Head, Letters and Science Extension, University of California Extension at Berkeley; Edwin H. Colbert, Curator, Department of Vertebrate Paleontology, The American Museum of Natural History; Raymond B. Cowles, Professor Emeritus of Zoology, University of California at Los Angeles; W. H. Dawbin, Senior Lecturer on Zoology, University of Sydney, Australia; Herndon Dowling, Curator of Reptiles, New York Zoological Park; James A. Fowler, Assistant Professor of Biological Sciences, State University of New York at Stony Brook; Carl Gans, Professor of Biology, State University of New York at Buffalo; Carl K. Kauffield, Curator of Reptiles, Staten Island Zoo; Samuel McDowell, Associate Professor of Zoology, Rutgers University; Alfred S. Romer, Alexander Agassiz Professor of Zoology, Harvard University; Charles E. Shaw, Curator of Reptiles, San Diego Zoological Garden; Richard C. Snyder, Professor of Zoology, University of Washington; Walter Dawn; John N. Hamlet; Bucky Reeves; Robert S. Simmons, D.D.S.; Charles J. Stine, D.D.S.; John H. Tashjian, and the New Zealand Consulate General, New York City.

Index

Numerals in italics indicate a photograph or painting of the subject mentioned.